Scott, Foresman Reading

Rainbow Shower

Program Authors

Ira E. Aaron
Dauris Jackson
Carole Riggs
Richard G. Smith
Robert J. Tierney

Book Authors

Joanna Cairns
Elizabeth Galloway
Robert J. Tierney

Instructional Consultants

John Manning
Dolores Perez

Scott, Foresman and Company
Editorial Offices: Glenview, Illinois

Regional Offices: Palo Alto, California
Tucker, Georgia • Glenview, Illinois
Oakland, New Jersey • Dallas, Texas

ACKNOWLEDGMENTS

"The Garden" from FROG AND TOAD TOGETHER by Arnold Lobel. Copyright © 1971, 1972 by Arnold Lobel. By permission of Harper & Row, Publishers, Inc. and World's Work, Ltd., The Windmill Press.

"Grandfather Frog" by Louise Seaman Bechtel is reprinted by permission of E. P. Dutton from ANOTHER HERE AND NOW STORY BOOK by Lucy Sprague Mitchell. Copyright, 1937, by E. P. Dutton and Co., Inc. Copyright renewal, 1965, by Lucy Sprague Mitchell.

"Millicent Maybe" adapted from MILLICENT MAYBE by Ellen Weiss, text copyright © 1979 by Ellen Weiss. Reprinted by permission of Franklin Watts, Inc.

"Ebbie" is a condensation and adaptation of EBBIE by Eve Rice. Copyright © 1975 by Eve Rice. By permission of Greenwillow Books (A Division of William Morrow & Company) and Curtis Brown, Ltd.

"Gwendolyn Brooks—A Child Alone" includes "Andre" and "Keziah" from BRONZEVILLE BOYS AND GIRLS by Gwendolyn Brooks. Copyright © 1956 by Gwendolyn Brooks Blakely. By permission of Harper & Row, Publishers, Inc.

"A Special Rock" from EVERYBODY NEEDS A ROCK by Byrd Baylor is used by permission of Charles Scribner's Sons and Toni Strassman, Agent. Copyright © 1974 by Byrd Baylor.

"I Meant to Do My Work Today" by Richard LeGallienne is reprinted by permission of DODD, MEAD & COMPANY, INC. and The Society of Authors as the literary representative of the Estate of Richard LeGallienne from THE LONELY DANCER AND OTHER POEMS by Richard LeGallienne. Copyright 1913 by Dodd, Mead & Company. Copyright renewed 1941 by Richard LeGallienne.

"Madge's Magic Show" is an adaptation of MADGE'S MAGIC SHOW by Mike Thaler, copyright © 1978 by Michael C. Thaler. Used by permission of Franklin Watts, Inc. and Curtis Brown, Ltd.

"That's What Friends Are For" is used by permission of Scholastic Book Services, a Division of Scholastic Magazines, Inc., from THAT'S WHAT FRIENDS ARE FOR by Florence Parry Heide and Sylvia Worth Van Clief, text copyright © 1968 by Florence Parry Heide and Sylvia Worth Van Clief.

"Do You Have the Time, Lydia?" is reprinted by permission of E. P. Dutton from DO YOU HAVE THE TIME, LYDIA? by Evaline Ness. Copyright © 1971 by Evaline Ness.

Untitled poem which begins "Old Cans, Boxes, Wire" from AND THE FROG WENT 'BLAH!' by Arnold Spilka, copyright 1972, by author's permission.

"Sound Around Us" by Louise Howard Brown includes material based on information from PROVE IT! by Rose Wyler and Gerald Ames. Text copyright © 1963 by Rose Wyler and Gerald Ames. By permission of Harper & Row, Publishers, Inc. and World's Work Limited, The Windmill Press.

"The Big Enormous Carrot" from "The Big Enormous Carrot" by Dorothy Gordon. Copyright © 1974, HIGHLIGHTS FOR CHILDREN, INC., Columbus, Ohio. Used by permission.

"Stone Soup" is adapted from STONE SOUP by Marcia Brown by permission of Charles Scribner's Sons. Copyright 1947 by Marcia Brown.

"The Flying Patchwork Quilt" from THE FLYING PATCHWORK QUILT by Barbara Brenner. Copyright 1965 by Barbara Brenner. Used by permission of the author.

From "The Kite" in WINDY MORNING, copyright 1953 by Harry Behn. Reprinted by permission of Harcourt Brace Jovanovich, Inc.

"Possum Was Fooled" by Shirley Patterson. Reprinted from Humpty Dumpty's Magazine. Copyright © 1967 by Parents' Magazine Enterprises, a division of Gruner + Jahr, U.S.A., Inc.

"The Magpie's Nest" is adapted from "The Magpie's Nest" from ENGLISH FAIRY TALES collected by Joseph Jacobs. Published by Schocken Books, Inc.

"The Mysterious Shadow" is an abridged and adapted version of THE MYSTERIOUS PROWLER, © 1976 by Joan Lowery Nixon. Reprinted by permission of Harcourt Brace Jovanovich, Inc.

"Poem" by Langston Hughes. Copyright 1923 and renewed 1960 by Langston Hughes. Reprinted from DREAM KEEPER AND OTHER POEMS, by Langston Hughes, by permission of Alfred A. Knopf, Inc.

"The New Girl in School" is adapted from THE NEW GIRL IN SCHOOL by Judy Delton. Copyright © 1979 by Judy Delton. Reprinted by permission of E. P. Dutton, publishers.

(Acknowledgments continued on page 272)

CONTENTS

SECTION TWO

SECTION ONE

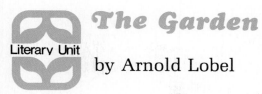

The Garden

by Arnold Lobel

Frog was in his garden. Toad came
walking by.

"What a fine garden you have, Frog,"
he said.

"Yes," said Frog. "It is very nice,
but it was hard work."

8

"I wish I had a garden," said Toad.

"Here are some flower seeds. Plant them in the ground," said Frog, "and soon you will have a garden."

"How soon?" asked Toad.

"Very soon," said Frog.

Toad ran home. He planted the flower seeds.

"Now seeds," said Toad, "start growing."

Toad walked up and down a few times. The seeds did not start to grow.

Toad put his head close to the ground and cried, "Now seeds, start growing!"

The seeds did not start to grow.

Toad put his head very close to the ground and shouted, "NOW SEEDS, START GROWING!"

Frog ran up the path. "What is going on?" he asked.

"My seeds will not grow," said Toad.

"You are shouting too much," said Frog. "These poor seeds are afraid to grow."

"My seeds are afraid to grow?" asked Toad.

"Yes," said Frog. "Leave them alone for a few days. Let the sun shine on them, let the rain fall on them. Soon your seeds will start to grow."

That night Toad looked out his window.

"Oh, no!" cried Toad. "My seeds have not started to grow. They must be afraid of the dark."

Toad went out to his garden.

"I will read the seeds a story," said
Toad.

Toad read a long story to his seeds.

All the next day Toad sang songs to his seeds.

And all the next day Toad read poems to his seeds.

And all the next day Toad played music for his seeds.

Toad looked at the ground. The seeds still did not start to grow.

"What shall I do?" cried Toad. "These seeds must be very frightened."

Then Toad became very tired, and he fell asleep.

"Toad, Toad, wake up," said Frog. "Look at your garden!"

Toad looked at his garden. Little green plants were growing up out of the ground.

"At last," shouted Toad, "my seeds have stopped being afraid to grow!"

"And now you will have a nice garden too," said Frog.

"Yes," said Toad, "but you were right, Frog. It was very hard work."

Comprehension Check

1. What four things did Toad do to make his seeds grow?
2. Why did Frog tell Toad to leave the seeds alone?
3. How do you think Toad felt about his garden? Why do you think as you do?
4. If you had a garden, what would you plant in it?

Grandfather Frog

by Louise Seaman Bechtel

Fat green frog sits by the pond,
Big frog, bull frog, grandfather frog.
Croak—croak—croak.
Shuts his eye, opens his eye,
Rolls his eye, winks his eye,
Waiting for
A little fat fly.

Croak, croak.
I go walking down by the pond,
I want to see the big green frog,
I want to stare right into his eye,
Rolling, winking, funny old eye.
But oh! he hears me coming by.
Croak—croak—
SPLASH!

Real or Make-Believe?

Some stories tell about things that could really happen. Other stories tell about make-believe things that could never really happen.

Read the two stories below.

Maria rode her bicycle to the store. On the way she saw many people. Some of the people waved to her. Maria also saw her friend Joel riding his bicycle. They rode to the store together.

Hilda Hippo put on her roller skates and skated to the store. On the way she met a large, orange lion. The lion was putting boxes of stardust on his truck. He smiled and waved at Hilda.

Which story could really happen? Which story could not really happen?

16

The story about Maria is real because it could really happen. The story about Hilda Hippo is make-believe because it could never really happen. What are the make-believe things in Hilda's story?

Practice

Now read this story.

The cat and the rabbit sat on a rock and ate their lunch. "The lettuce and carrots are good," said the rabbit.

The cat said, "My fish soup is good too." Then the cat gave the rabbit some of his milk. "Here, try some of this," the cat said.

Is the story real or make-believe? Why do you think so?

Read the next story. Is "Millicent Maybe" real or make-believe?

Millicent Maybe

by Ellen Weiss

Millicent Maybe lived all alone. She could cook what she pleased. And buy what she pleased. And go where she pleased. But she could never make up her mind.

"I wonder what I should eat," said Millicent each morning.

"Maybe an orange.

Or maybe pancakes.

Or maybe some toast."

Millicent could not decide.

So she ate a little of this and a little of that.

18

"I wonder what I should wear today," said Millicent.

"Maybe it will rain.

Or maybe the sun will shine.

Maybe it will be cold.

Or maybe it will be hot."

Millicent could not decide.

So she wore a little of this and a little of that.

It was maybe this and maybe that at the book store. It was maybe this and maybe that at the shoe store. It was maybe this and maybe that at the food store.

Soon Millicent had eaten too much of this and too much of that. She could not fit into anything.

She had bought too much of this and too much of that. There was hardly enough room left for Millicent.

"If only I had somebody to tell me what to do!" said Millicent.

Just then she saw an ad in the morning
newspaper.

"That's it!" shouted Millicent, as she
put down the newspaper.

"That's just what I need!"

And she ran to the pet shop.

"I wonder what I should do," said Millicent.

There were so many parrots, Millicent could not decide which one to buy. So she took them all.

"I'll never have to make up my mind again," said Millicent. "Now I'll have somebody to talk to. These parrots will tell me what to do!"

And they did.

As soon as she got home the yellow parrot flew to Millicent and began to cry,

"TAKE A BATH! TAKE A BATH!"

"Whatever you say!" said Millicent. And she ran upstairs to take a bath.

Then the green parrot flew over and shouted,

"MAKE SOME POPCORN! POPCORN! POPCORN!"

"Whatever you say!" said Millicent. And she ran back down to make some popcorn.

"STAND ON YOUR HEAD!"

said the blue parrot.

"Whatever you say!" said Millicent. And she turned upside down.

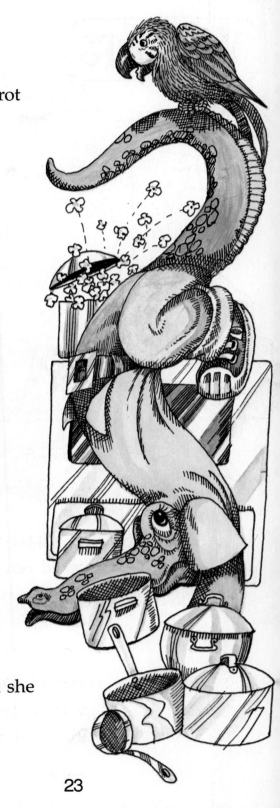

And then she heard it!

Splash! Splash! Splash!

Pop! Pop! Pop!

"Oh, no!" said Millicent. "My bath! My popcorn!"

"Help!" shouted Millicent. "What should I do?"

"GO TO SLEEP!"

"CHIRP LIKE A BIRD!"

"COOK PANCAKES!"

"Stop it!" shouted Millicent. "I can't stand it anymore!"

Then, for the very first time, Millicent made up her mind. She opened the window. The parrots flew out.

"Good-by, parrots!" said Millicent. "I can think for myself!"

She opened the front door. All the tables and chairs floated out of the house. And all the popcorn and other food floated after them. Then Millicent floated out too.

Her neighbors ran to help.

"Shall we carry it all back inside?" they asked.

"No, thank you," said Millicent. "I don't need a little of this and a little of that. I'll decide what I like best."

Millicent decided what to keep and what to give away.

Then Millicent went indoors and sat down in her best chair.

She wore her very best dress and her very best hat.

She thought of all the things she used to have.

And she did not miss them at all.

Comprehension Check

1. What did Millicent Maybe see in the morning newspaper?
2. Why did Millicent make popcorn?
3. Did the parrots help Millicent? Why do you think as you do?
4. What can you do if you have trouble making up your mind?

Skill Check

1. Is this story real or make-believe?
2. What are some of the things in the story that make you think as you do?

EBBIE

by Eve Rice

When Eddie was little, he lived in an apartment house. And he had a little sister named Emma.

One day Emma pulled him and he fell down. She did not mean to do it, but his two front teeth fell out all the same.

After that, Edward called himself "Ebbie" because it was very hard to say "Eddie" with no front teeth.

And everybody else called him "Ebbie" too—Mama, Papa, Grandma, Uncle Arthur, and his little sister, Emma.

When Edward was a little bigger, he did not like being called "Ebbie" so much anymore. He learned to say "Eddie" without his two front teeth.

But no one else learned. They still called him "Ebbie." That made him very angry.

"Ebbie," said Mama.

"I am not Ebbie!" he said.

"Ebbie," said Papa.

"You mean Eddie!" said Edward.

"Where is Ebbie?" Uncle Arthur asked one morning.

Nobody knew.

So they went looking. They looked in the hall. No Ebbie. But somebody had written "Eddie!" on a piece of paper and taped it to the hall table.

They walked down the hall to little Emma's room. No Ebbie. But somebody had written "Eddie!" on a piece of paper and taped it to Emma's wall.

"Where else could Ebbie be?" asked Uncle Arthur.

"I wish I knew," said Grandma.

30

They looked in Edward's room. No Ebbie.
But somebody had written "Eddie!" on a piece
of paper and taped it to the wall.

"My, my!" said Uncle Arthur.

"Where can Ebbie be?" asked Papa.

Mama thought for a little while.

"You mean, where can Eddie be?" she said.

"Yes, I guess I do," said Papa. "And if
I had such a nice name, I would not go away."

"I wish I knew where Eddie was,"
everybody said together.

And then Papa thought he heard something move.

And Mama thought she heard a little laugh.

But everybody was sure they heard someone under the bed say "Eddie!" very loudly.

And there he was.

"Eddie!" said Edward.

"OUR EDDIE!" said Mama, Papa, Grandma, Uncle Arthur, and little Emma.

And after that, nobody called him "Ebbie" anymore. Nobody, that is, but his little sister Emma, and that was OK because it is very hard to say "Eddie" with no front teeth.

33

Comprehension Check

1. Why did Eddie call himself "Ebbie" in the beginning of the story?
2. Why did Eddie hide under the bed one morning?
3. Why do you think Eddie didn't like being called "Ebbie" anymore?
4. If you could choose a nickname for yourself, what would it be?

Skill Check

Read the sentences below. What do the underlined words stand for?

1. Mama thought for a little while.
   "You mean, where can Eddie be?" she said.
   a. Eddie   b. Mama
2. And then Papa thought he heard something move.
   a. Papa   b. Eddie

Word Puzzles

When you read, you may see a word you don't know. How can you tell what the word is? First try to think of a word that makes sense in the sentence you are reading. Then see if the consonant sounds in your word match the consonant sounds in the word you don't know.

Decide what word fits in each sentence.

1. Jessie loves to p_____ pictures in her scrapbook.

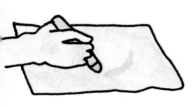  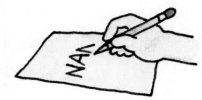

2. She found a picture of a cute p____pp____.

3. She put in a story about a l___n that
   lives in the zoo.

Did your word choices make sense in the
sentences? Did your word choices match the
consonant clues? The words <u>paste</u>, <u>puppy</u>, and
<u>lion</u> fit in the sentences.

Practice

Now read these sentences. Use the clues
in each sentence to find the word that fits.

1. Jessie puts her pictures in a n_____.

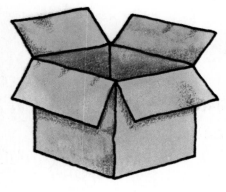

2. She is happy when her f___th___r likes
   the pictures.

3. Jessie read a story about a r_____t
   that flew to the moon.

Which words make sense in each sentence?
Which word matches the consonant clues?

Read the next story about Gwendolyn Brooks.
Use the steps you have just learned to figure out
any word you do not know.

Gwendolyn Brooks—
A Child Alone

by Deborah Finley-Jackson

Keziah

I have a secret place to go.
Not anyone may know.
And sometimes when the wind is rough
I cannot get there fast enough.
And sometimes when my mother
Is scolding my big brother,
My secret place, it seems to me,
Is quite the only place to be.

Gwendolyn Brooks

When Gwendolyn Brooks was a little girl,
she had a special place of her own. Gwendolyn
went there almost every day. Sometimes she
read. But most of the time she wrote poems.

One day her mother opened the back door.

"There's a fire a few houses down," she called. Gwendolyn looked up from her writing just long enough to see many people rushing to see the fire. But she did not move.

Gwendolyn did not want to see the fire. She wanted to write a poem. Gwendolyn wrote another line. Her mind was far away from the fire. She was alone, but she was happy. She was happy because she was writing a poem.

Gwendolyn was seven when she wrote her first poem. She lived in Hyde Park, Illinois, with her mother, father, and brother. Everybody in her family was very proud of her. But her mother helped her the most.

Every time Mrs. Brooks read one of Gwendolyn's poems she said, "It's good! It's very, very good! I'm proud to be your mother. And someday everybody will know your name."

As Gwendolyn got older she wrote more and more poems. She was also alone more and more, and the other children didn't understand.

"That Gwendolyn Brooks," they said. "All she wants to do is write. She never wants to do anything with us."

In a way Gwendolyn did want to be with the other children. But she also wanted to stay in her secret place and write. Gwendolyn knew that one day she would be glad she had worked so hard.

"One day," she said often, "I will see my name next to a poem in a book."

40

Gwendolyn went to college for two years. While she was there, she wrote as many poems as she could. Every week she went to a poetry class. She read her work to the other people in the class. Then she listened to what they had to say.

Most of the time the class liked Gwendolyn's poems. One day they picked the best poem in the class. Gwendolyn's poem got first prize.

Gwendolyn was very happy when some of
her poems were made into a poetry book. It
was her first book, and it was about the
place where she lived.

When her family heard about the book,
they were very proud. It was special to have
a poet in the family.

Now Gwendolyn Brooks is a famous poet. She is often asked to talk to children about her poetry. She talks about what it was like when she was growing up. She tells the children about her family, her secret place, and the children that she knew. Then she reads some of her poetry, like the poem on the next page.

Andre

I had a dream last night. I dreamed
I had to pick a Mother out.
I had to choose a Father too.
At first, I wondered what to do,
There were so many there, it seemed,
Short and tall and thin and stout.

But just before I sprang awake,
I knew what parents I would take.

And <u>this</u> surprised and made me glad:
They were the ones I always had.

Gwendolyn Brooks

Comprehension Check

1. How old was Gwendolyn when she wrote her first poem?
2. Why did Gwendolyn's poem win first prize?
3. How do you think Gwendolyn's mother felt about Gwendolyn's poetry?
4. Is there anything that you like to do as much as Gwendolyn liked to write poems? What is it?

Skill Check

Which word fits in each of these sentences?

1. Mrs. Brooks was very pr_____ of Gwendolyn.

   print   proud   sure

2. Gwendolyn has won many pr_____.

   pretty   prizes   races

3. Gwendolyn had a sp_____ place.

   spots   nice   special

A Special Rock

adapted from a book by Byrd Baylor

Everybody
needs
a rock.

I'm sorry for kids
who don't have
a rock
for a friend.
That's why
I'm telling them
my own
TEN RULES
for
finding
a
rock. . . .

46   *Literary Unit*

Not
just
any rock.
I mean
a
special
rock
that you find
all alone
and keep
as long as
you can—
maybe
forever.

If somebody happens to say,
"What's so special
about that rock?"
don't even tell them.
I don't.

Nobody
should know
what's so special
about
somebody else's
rock.

All right.
Here
are
the
rules:

RULE NUMBER 1

If you can,
go to a mountain
made out of
hundreds and
hundreds of
small
beautiful
rocks.

But if you can't,
any place will do.

RULE NUMBER 2

When you are looking
at rocks,
don't let
mothers or fathers
or sisters or brothers
or even best friends
talk
to you.
You should choose
a rock
when everything
is quiet and easy.
Don't let dogs bark
at you
or bees buzz
at you.

RULE NUMBER 3

Bend over.
More.
Even more.
You may have to
sit
on the ground
with your head
almost
touching
the earth.
You have to look
a rock
right
in the eye.
Or
don't blame me
if you
can't find
a good one.

RULE NUMBER 4

Don't get a rock
that is
too big.
You'll
always
be sorry.
It won't fit
your hand
right
and it won't fit
your pocket.

A rock as big as
an orange
is too big.
A rock as big as
a horse
is
MUCH
too big.

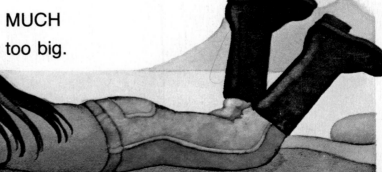

RULE NUMBER 5

Don't choose a rock
that is
too small.
It will only be
easy
to lose
or
a mouse
might eat it,
thinking
that it
is a seed.
(I know,
because
that happened
to a boy
in the state
of Arizona.)

RULE NUMBER 6

The size
must be
perfect.
It has to feel
easy
in your hand
when you close
your fingers
over it.
It has to feel
jumpy
in your pocket
when you run.

Some people
touch a rock
a hundred times
a day.
There aren't many things
that feel
as good as a rock—
if the rock
is
perfect.

RULE NUMBER 7

Look for
the perfect
color.
Some rocks
that look brown
are really other
colors,
but
you only see them
when you squint
and when the sun
is right.

Another way
to see colors
is to dip
your rock
in a clean
mountain stream—
if one is passing by.

RULE NUMBER 8

The shape
of the rock
is up to you.

The thing to remember
about shapes
is this:
Any rock
looks good
with a hundred
other rocks
around it on a hill.
But
if your rock
is going to be special
it should look good
all alone
in the bath.

RULE NUMBER 9

Always
sniff
a rock.
Rocks have
their own smells.

You'll find out that
mothers and fathers
can't tell these things.
Too bad for them.
They just can't
smell as well
as kids can.

RULE NUMBER 10

Don't ask anyone
to help you choose.

I've seen
a lizard
pick one rock
out of
a desert full
of rocks
and go sit there
alone.
I've seen
a snail
pass up
ten rocks
and spend all day
getting to
the one
it wanted.

You have to
make up
your own mind.
You'll
<u>know</u>.

All right,
that's
ten rules.
If you think
of any more
write them down.
I'm going out
to play a game
that takes
just me
and one rock
to play.

I happen to have
a rock here in my hand. . . .

Comprehension Check

1. Where is a good place to find a rock?

2. Why should you choose a rock that is just the right size?

3. Do you think it is good to be alone when you choose your rock? Why or why not?

4. What kinds of things do you like to collect? Tell your rules for collecting things.

I Meant To Do My Work Today

by Richard LeGallienne

I meant to do my work today—
But a brown bird sang in the apple tree,
And a butterfly flitted across the field,
And all the leaves were calling me.

And the wind went sighing over the land
Tossing the grasses to and fro,
And a rainbow held out its shining hand—
So what could I do but laugh and go?

MADGE'S MAGIC SHOW

by Mike Thaler

Madge was very special. She was a
great magician. She had a hat, a cape,
and a wand.

One day she decided to give a magic
show. People came from far away. But not
Jimmy Smith. He just looked over the fence.

Madge smiled and waved her wand.
"Abracadabra. Sky and stars. Get set to
see some magic. I'm Madge the Magnifico!"

56

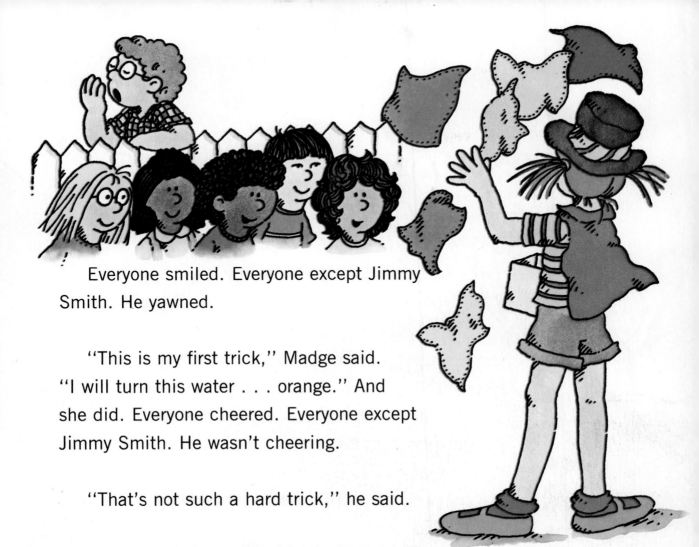

Everyone smiled. Everyone except Jimmy Smith. He yawned.

"This is my first trick," Madge said. "I will turn this water . . . orange." And she did. Everyone cheered. Everyone except Jimmy Smith. He wasn't cheering.

"That's not such a hard trick," he said.

Madge looked over the fence. She stuck up her nose and turned her back.

"As you can see," she said, "there is nothing in this box. I will now pull six scarves out of it."

And she did.

Everyone smiled and cheered. Everyone
except Jimmy Smith.

"Scarves are silly," he said.

"Scarves are NOT silly," said Madge.
She pulled back her cape and took off her
hat.

"And now if you'll be quiet," she said,
"I will do the best trick that you have
ever seen. I will pull a small white rabbit
out of this very hat!"

58

"That's silly," said Jimmy Smith. "You can't pull a rabbit out of that hat."

"Ready?" asked Madge. Then she smiled, said her magic words, reached into her hat, and pulled out . . .

a duck!

"That's the best trick I've ever seen!" said Freddy Jones.

"Where did you learn *that*?" asked Peter Wong.

"A duck is not a rabbit," said Jimmy Smith.

"Quiet!" said Madge. "I need a little time! OK. Ready?"

"Ready," said Jimmy Smith.

Madge said the magic words and waved her wand. Then she reached back into her hat and pulled out . . .

a turkey!

"*That's* the best trick I've ever seen," said Freddy Jones.

"Where did you learn *that*?" asked Peter Wong.

"That's silly!" said Jimmy Smith. "A turkey is NOT a rabbit!"

Madge's face turned red. She waved her hand and called for quiet. Then she reached in and pulled out . . .

a goat!

The goat began to eat Madge's cape. Everybody laughed. Everybody except Jimmy Smith. He wasn't laughing.

"I knew she couldn't do it!" he said.

"One more time," Madge said. "Are you ready?"

"Ready," said Jimmy Smith.

Madge said the magic words and waved her wand. Then she reached into her hat and pulled out . . .

a horse!

"Wow! A horse!" said Ana Santos.

"Now I've seen everything," said Freddy Jones.

"Where did you learn THAT?" asked Peter Wong.

"I told you she couldn't do it," said Jimmy Smith.

62

Madge put on her hat. "I guess the show is over," she said. She put on what was left of her cape.

Just then the hat began to move. A little pink nose stuck out from under it.

"A rabbit!" said Madge. "What took you so long?"

The little rabbit jumped to the ground and everyone cheered.

"Wow!" said Jimmy Smith. "That's a rabbit all right. How did you do it?"

"It was nothing," said Madge. "All we great magicians know how."

Comprehension Check

1. Did everyone like the magic tricks that Madge did? Explain your answer.
2. Why did Madge stick up her nose and turn her back on Jimmy Smith?
3. How do you think Madge felt when Jimmy Smith made fun of her?
4. What kind of show or play would you like to put on?

Skill Check

What is the root word and the ending in each of the words below?

looked	yawned	cheered	cheering
turned	pulled	reached	laughing

What Is It All About?

Every story has a main idea. The **main idea** is what the story is all about. Sometimes one sentence in a story tells the main idea. That sentence may be the first or last sentence in the story. It may also be in the middle of the story.

Read the story below. Look for one sentence that tells you what the story is about.

Hector is a runner. He wears special running shoes. In the morning, he runs to school. At noon, he runs around the playground. After school, he runs home and plays with his friends.

Which sentence tells you the main idea of the story? You'll find the main idea in the first sentence, Hector is a runner.

Practice

Now read this story.

The children were having fun. Some boys and girls were running a race. Tina and Fred were playing tag. Ann was playing hide-and-seek with her friends. Ten girls and boys were playing basketball.

What is the main idea of the story?

a. It was a wonderful day.

b. Tina and Fred were playing tag.

c. The children were having fun.

Remember that every story has a main idea. Look for the main idea in the next story about an elephant. The main idea will help you understand the story.

That's What Friends Are For

by Florence Parry Heide
and Sylvia Worth Van Clief

Theodore, the elephant, is sitting in the middle of the forest. He has hurt his leg. What a problem! This morning Theodore was going to meet his cousin at the end of the forest.

"What can I do?" Theodore says. "My cousin is at the end of the forest, and here I am in the middle of the forest. And I have a bad leg, and I can't walk."

"I know what I'll do," Theodore says. "I'll ask my friends for advice. That's what friends are for."

Along comes Theodore's friend, the bird.

"Why are you sitting here in the middle of the forest?" asks the bird.

"I have a problem," says Theodore. "I have a bad leg, and I can't walk. And I can't meet my cousin at the end of the forest."

"If *I* had a bad leg, I would fly to the end of the forest," says the bird to Theodore.

"It's nice of you to give advice," says Theodore to the bird.

"That's what friends are for," says the bird.

Along comes Theodore's friend, the daddy-long-legs.

"Why are you sitting here in the middle of the forest?" asks the daddy-long-legs.

"I have a problem," says Theodore. "I have a bad leg, and I can't walk. And I can't fly. And I can't meet my cousin at the end of the forest."

"If *I* had a bad leg," says the daddy-long-legs, "*I* could walk because I have seven *other* legs."

"It's nice of you to give advice," says Theodore.

"That's what friends are for," says the daddy-long-legs.

70

Along comes Theodore's friend, the monkey.

"Why are you sitting here in the middle of the forest?" asks the monkey.

"I have a problem," says Theodore. "I have a bad leg, and I can't walk. And I can't fly. And I don't have seven other legs. And I can't meet my cousin at the end of the forest."

"If *I* had a bad leg," says the monkey, "I would swing by my tail from the trees, like this."

"Well," says Theodore, "I may have a very weak *tail*, but I have a very strong *trunk*."

Theodore grabs a branch of the tree with his trunk . . . CRASH!

"Well," says Theodore, "thank you for your advice, just the same."

"That's what friends are for," says the monkey.

Along comes Theodore's friend, the crab.

"Why are you sitting in the middle of the forest?" asks the crab.

"I have a problem," says Theodore. "I have a bad leg, and I can't walk. And I can't fly. And I don't have seven other legs. And I can't swing from the trees by my tail (OR my trunk). And I can't meet my cousin at the end of the forest."

"If *I* had a bad leg," says the crab, "I would get rid of it and grow another one."

"It's nice of you to give advice," says Theodore.

"That's what friends are for," says the crab.

Along comes Theodore's friend, the lion.

"Why are you sitting here in the middle of the forest?" asks the lion.

"I have a problem," says Theodore. "I have a bad leg, and I can't walk. And I can't fly. And I don't have seven other legs. And I can't swing from the trees by my tail (OR my trunk). And I can't grow another leg. And I can't meet my cousin at the end of the forest."

74

"If *I* had a bad leg," says the lion, "I would roar so that everybody in the forest would hear me and run over to see what was the matter."

And he roars.

"What is happening here?" the opossum asks.

Everybody starts to talk at once.

"Theodore has a problem," says the bird. "He can't fly."

"He can't get to the end of the forest to see his cousin," says the lion. "We are giving him advice. That's what friends are for."

"No," says the opossum. "Friends should help. *That's* what friends are for. Let's bring the cousin to Theodore."

So all the friends go to find Theodore's
cousin at the end of the forest. And everybody
brings the cousin to Theodore.

"Thank you for *helping* me," says Theodore to
his friends.

"That's what friends are for," say the
friends.

To give advice is very nice,
but friends can do much more.
Friends should always help a friend.
That's what friends are for!

Comprehension Check

1. What was Theodore's problem?
2. What was the crab's advice? Why wasn't it helpful to Theodore?
3. Which friend was the most helpful? How did this animal help Theodore?
4. Have you ever helped a good friend? How?

Skill Check

What is the main idea of the story?

a. Everyone has problems.
b. An elephant with a bad leg should learn to roar.
c. Friends should help each other.

A DOG FOR MARIA

by Linda Beech

It is a beautiful spring day in the city and
Maria is up early. Maria knows that it is a nice
day because she can smell the spring flowers.
She can feel the warm sun and hear the birds
singing.

But Maria can't see the spring day. She can't
see the green trees or the blue sky. Maria can't
see colors because she is blind. She has always
been blind.

Far away, Shep is up early too. Shep is a young dog who goes to a special school in the country. At this school Shep learns to help blind people. Shep is a guide dog. He has been at the guide school for four months.

Today Maria will go to the country to meet Shep. She will live at Shep's school for a month. While she is there, she will work with Shep every day. Shep will learn to be her guide. They will leave the school together.

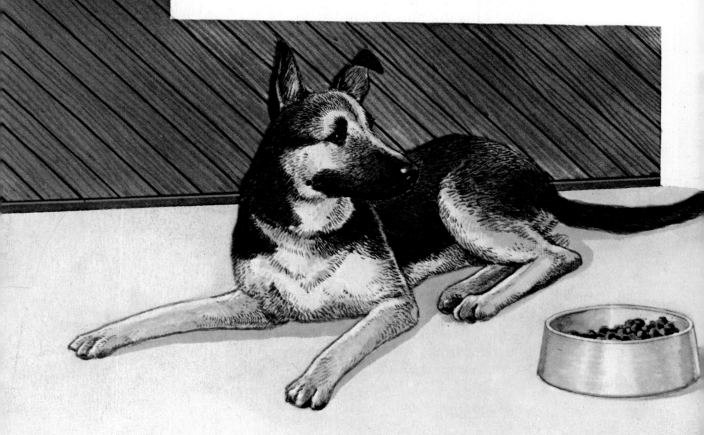

When Maria meets Shep for the first time, she can feel that he is a friend. She loves dogs and she is not afraid.

"Hello, Shep," she says. "I guess we're a family now." Then she gives him a big hug. Maria can tell by his bark that Shep is happy too. The teachers think Shep and Maria will work well together.

Early the next day Maria and Shep are ready to start their training.

Shep has a special collar and Maria learns how to hold it. Then she learns how to talk to Shep so that he can guide her. Shep knows what it means when he hears Maria say "Sit," "Stay," and other words. And he knows what it means when Maria pulls on his collar. Shep has been learning these things for four months.

Shep and Maria learn to walk together. At first they walk along country roads where it is quiet. When they are in the country, Shep guides Maria around things.

82

When Maria feels ready, they walk in the city. They learn to go into stores and other places. Shep always makes sure that Maria doesn't bump into anyone.

Learning to cross a city street is not easy. When Maria hears the cars, she stops. Then, when the street is quiet, she lets Shep know that it is time to cross.

If Maria tells Shep to cross when a car is coming, Shep will not move. His job is to keep Maria safe. He will not guide Maria across the street until he is sure they are safe.

Maria has things to learn too. She must learn to feed Shep well. And she must learn to keep him clean and happy. But most of all, Maria must remember to tell Shep that he is doing a good job. Shep is a smart dog, and most of the time Maria is pleased with him. She gives Shep a hug and talks to him in a quiet tone. But Shep is also young, and sometimes he does things wrong.

When they are not working, Maria and Shep play together. Before long they grow to love each other.

Guide dogs are not for everyone. Some blind people don't love dogs. Some don't feel safe with them. Some people are too old and some are too young. But Maria is just right. She is glad about that.

And so is Shep.

Comprehension Check

1. Why can't Maria see the spring day? How does she know it is a nice day?
2. How does Shep know when to cross a street?
3. Why do you think Maria must remember to tell Shep that he is doing a good job?
4. Have you ever heard of a pet that helped someone? What did the pet do?

Skill Check

Look at the list of words below.

can	pet	nice	time
safe	at	not	sit

1. Which words in the list have long vowel sounds?
2. Which words have short vowel sounds? What letter could you add to each of these words to change the vowel sound from short to long?

Do You Have the Time, Lydia?

by Evaline Ness

Once there was a little girl named Lydia. She lived with her father and her brother Andy at the beach.

Lydia was always very busy. One minute she was writing a story. The next she was learning a new game. One minute she was reading the morning newspaper. The next minute she was turning sand into a mountain. Lydia never remembered to finish anything.

Her father always said, "If you take the time, you can have the time." But Lydia was too busy to listen.

Andy wasn't busy doing anything, because he didn't know how. If he asked Lydia to help him fix something, she said, "I can't. I don't have the time."

One morning Andy was splashing along the beach and he found an old lobster trap. He pulled it home. Lydia was sitting in her room. She was writing on a piece of paper.

"Look," Andy shouted, as he pulled the trap through the door. "I found a perfect car for the race! Please, Lydia. Fix it for me so I can be in Dr. Arnold's race. The newspaper said the prize is a dog."

"I can't," said Lydia, without looking up. "I don't have the time."

"But the race is today!" Andy told his sister. "You can fix it in time. Please."

"Well, all right. I'll fix it. But not now."

"I knew it!" cried Andy. "You're always too busy."

"Look, Andy. Writing a story is not easy. As a matter of fact, it is very hard work. But I said I'll fix it and I mean I'll fix it."

Andy looked hard at Lydia. Then he backed out of the room.

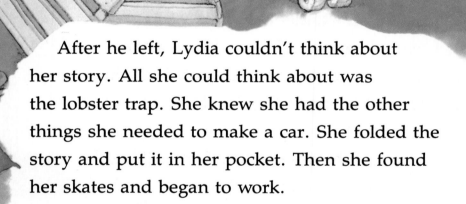

After he left, Lydia couldn't think about
her story. All she could think about was
the lobster trap. She knew she had the other
things she needed to make a car. She folded the
story and put it in her pocket. Then she found
her skates and began to work.

She pulled off the wheels and put them on
the corners of the trap. Then she cut two round
pieces of paper and taped them on the front for
lights. When she finished the lights, she found
a box for the driver to sit on.

"Perfect!" said Lydia. "Andy will love it!
All it needs is a steering wheel. I know *just*
where to find one that fits."

Lydia ran to the garage. In one corner she saw an old wheel. Next to it was a large glass dish.

"All *that* needs," said Lydia, "is a little water and a few small fish."

Lydia forgot about the wheel and raced down to the beach. When she was almost there, she saw a beautiful gull by the water. His eyes were closed and one wing was bent under him. All of a sudden he cried out. His wing flew up and hit her in the face.

"You need help!" shouted Lydia. "And I know just where to find it."

She left the gull and ran off to find Dr. Arnold. But nobody was at his house. A piece of paper was taped to the door. Dr. Arnold had written:

BACK SOON. I AM WORKING AT THE RACE.

The race! All of a sudden Lydia remembered Andy. She ran up the road. Andy was at the top of the hill, alone. The race was over. Dr. Arnold was handing the prize dog to a very happy girl. The other children were cheering.

Andy looked at Lydia. His eyes were big and cold. Lydia hugged him but he pulled away. Then he turned and ran.

"Wait, Andy," cried Lydia. "I'm so sorry. I really mean it. I was fixing the car but I didn't have enough time to finish."

But Andy didn't stop. He didn't look back.

Lydia waited until he turned the corner.
Then she walked back to Dr. Arnold's house.
She sat on the ground and put her head in
her hands. She had never felt this bad
before. Now she knew how Andy felt.

All of a sudden somebody said, "Can I
help?"

It was Dr. Arnold. The smile on his face
was warm and kind. It made her feel better.

Then Lydia remembered the gull.

"The gull!" she shouted. "Dr. Arnold!
It's on the beach and it's hurt!"

Dr. Arnold followed Lydia to the beach.
Dr. Arnold gave the gull something to make
it sleep. Then he fixed its wing with a
piece of tape.

At last he said, "It will be fine. But
it can't fly for a few days. I wonder if
you would like to take it home. That is,
if you have enough time."

"I'd love to," Lydia said. "And I'll
take the time."

94

Lydia hugged the gull to her and walked home. She put the gull in a bed she made for it. Then she thought about Andy.

She wanted to do something nice for him. It was too late to make a car for the race. But it wasn't too late to make a special car just for Andy.

Lydia went back to the garage. She took down the wheel. As she was going out of the garage, she saw a little house that she had started a long time ago.

"What this house needs . . ." Then she looked at the wheel and said, ". . . is nothing."

Lydia ran out of the garage and up to her room.

She had just finished fixing the wheel when she heard somebody. It was Andy. He was in the hall. "I don't want that old trap," he said.

"It's not a trap," Lydia said. "It's your very own special car. I'll make it a beautiful red color. And I'll write your name on it. You'll love it. Really you will."

96

"Do you mean it?" Andy asked his sister. "Will you really have enough time?"

Lydia bent over and hugged Andy. Then she said, "If I *take* the time, I can *have* the time." And she did.

Comprehension Check

1. Why did Lydia say that she couldn't make Andy a car for the race?
2. Why did Lydia go to see Dr. Arnold?
3. What kind of person do you think Lydia is?
4. What is the most interesting thing you have ever made?

Old cans, boxes, wire
And any old junk
   is good
If you want to make
   some sculpture.
You can make a cow
   . . . or a horse
or maybe even a vulture.

You can stick
    them together
or tie them
    with some string,
And if it doesn't
    Look like a real animal
At least it will look
    like SOMETHING.

Arnold Spilka

What Happened and Why?

Words such as <u>because</u> and <u>since</u> can work as clues in stories. They can tell you that you are about to find out why something happened.

Read the story below.

It was a nice day. Lucy and her mother went sailing. They were in the middle of the lake when the wind started to blow. The boat rocked from side to side because of the high waves. Lucy and her mother turned the boat around since they did not want to get wet.

Why did the boat rock from side to side? Look for the clue word <u>because</u> in the fourth sentence. Why did Lucy and her mother turn the boat around? What clue words helped you find the answers?

100

Practice

Now read this story.

Lucy was looking for shells on the beach. She suddenly stopped walking because she felt something under her foot. Lucy picked up her foot since she wanted to see what was there. She was surprised to find a beautiful shell. She took the shell because it was so special.

Answer these questions.

1. Why did Lucy suddenly stop walking?
2. Why did Lucy pick up her foot?
3. Why did Lucy take the shell?

Look for clue words like <u>since</u> and <u>because</u> in the next story about sounds. The clue words can help you find out why things happened.

Sound Around Us

by Louise Howard Brown

There are sounds all around us. Even when it is quiet, there is some sound. Sometimes we don't hear sounds because they are very soft. Sometimes we don't hear sounds because we are not listening for them. But the sounds are there.

What makes sounds happen? The next pages will help you find out.

Sounds happen because something moves. The top of a drum makes a sound because you hit it and it moves. A bell makes a sound because you shake it or hit it and it moves. A bee makes a buzzing sound because its wings are moving.

This movement is called *vibration*.

You can see and feel vibrations with a rubber band. Cut a rubber band and stretch it between your hands. Then ask a friend to pluck the rubber band. When the rubber band moves, or vibrates, it makes a sound. If you pluck the rubber band in different places, you will hear different sounds. Watch the rubber band when you pluck it. You can see why sounds happen.

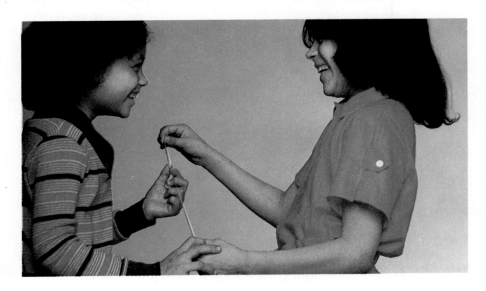

You can see a ruler vibrate too. You can even play songs on a ruler. To do this you need a very light ruler and a desk or table.

Hold the ruler on the side of the desk, like this.

Push the tip down with your other hand. Then let it go. Listen for the sound the ruler makes. Now move the ruler back so that most of it is on the desk. Push it down again. Do you hear a different sound? You can make many different sounds. Move the ruler up and back to make different sounds. You can make the ruler sing.

What makes the ruler sing? The ruler sings because it moves up and down in the air. When the ruler stops moving, the singing stops too.

When the ruler moves up and down, it vibrates, just like the rubber band. You can see the ruler vibrate. You can feel it vibrate with your finger. And you can hear the sounds that the ruler makes.

Have you ever listened to a balloon crying?
Blow up a balloon. Then pinch the neck and pull
it a little. If you let some air out, the balloon
will sound as if it is crying.

A balloon cries because the neck of the
balloon vibrates as air passes through it. You
can see the neck move, and you can feel it too.

Put your hand on your throat to feel the
sound of your own voice. Make some noises or say
some words. Can you feel your throat vibrate
when you make noises? Can you feel the sound of
your own voice? Your throat is vibrating since
air is passing through it as you talk.

When you stop talking, the vibrations stop.
And when vibrations stop, sounds stop too.

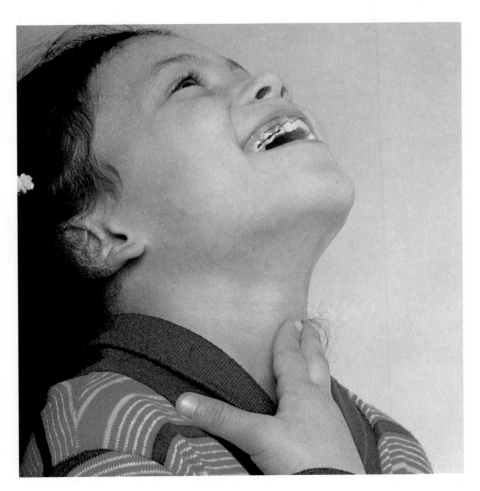

Comprehension Check

1. How can you play songs on a ruler?
2. Why do we sometimes not hear sounds when they are all around us?
3. Why do sounds happen?
4. What are some sounds that you don't like? What are some of the sounds that you like?

Skill Check

1. Why does a bee make a buzzing sound?
2. Why does a balloon cry when you let some air out?
3. Why does your throat vibrate when you talk?

The Big Enormous Carrot

by Dorothy Gordon

Victor loved his garden. He worked hard in
it and it made him very proud. He had big
round heads of lettuce, bright red radishes,
and other things too. But the nicest things in
his garden were his carrots, and they were
all big and fat and orange.

One day Victor pulled a big enormous carrot
out of the ground. It was very heavy.

"That's the biggest carrot I have ever seen," said Victor early one morning. "And it's all mine."

Then he had an idea. "I know. I'll take it to the fair. It will be the finest carrot at the fair and maybe I'll win a prize."

Victor washed the carrot carefully. He put it down to dry. Then he went into the house to get a bag.

That day Wiggly, Mr. Jones's big rabbit, got out of his cage again. He hopped into Victor's garden. He saw the big enormous carrot on the ground and began to eat it. It was good.

110

Victor came out of the house with his bag.
He saw Wiggly eating his carrot.

"Go away, you impossible rabbit!" he
shouted. "This garden is mine! Now get out!"

Wiggly kept right on eating the big
enormous carrot.

"Get out of here!" Victor shouted again.
"I said that carrot is mine."

But Wiggly kept on eating.

Mr. Jones raced across the yard. "What's
the matter?" he cried. Then he saw Wiggly.

"So here you are. I've been looking all
over for you."

"I got up very early this morning," Mr.
Jones told Victor, "and just as I got into my
bath I heard Wiggly. He was trying to get out
of his cage again. I jumped out of the bath and
looked out of the window, but he was gone.
What's he been up to?"

"He's been eating my enormous carrot," said Victor. "It was round and heavy and beautiful. Now Wiggly is round and heavy, and my carrot is nothing. I was going to take it to the fair and win a prize. But now that's impossible."

"I'm really sorry," said Mr. Jones. "But nothing is impossible. There has to be *something* we can do."

"No," said Victor. "There is nothing."

112

Wiggly kept eating and eating. At last he was finished. He sat up and flapped his ears. Then he hopped into the garage and went to sleep.

Mr. Jones was thinking. All of a sudden he smiled and said, "Wait a minute. I think I have an idea. Your carrot can go to the fair after all. And you might even win a prize."

"That's silly," said Victor. "How can my carrot win a prize when it's inside Wiggly?"

"I'll give you Wiggly," said Mr. Jones. "He's been a good pet, but he's your rabbit now. You can take Wiggly to the fair, and he might win a prize for you."

"Do you really mean it?" Victor cried.

"Really," said Mr. Jones.

Victor smiled. "That's a great idea," he said.

Then he went into the garage to find Wiggly.

Early the next morning, Victor picked up Wiggly and carried him to the fair. The rabbit felt heavy.

Wiggly was the best rabbit there, and he won first prize. Everybody cheered, and Victor felt happy and proud. Victor got a trophy. A little gold rabbit was sitting on top of the trophy. The rabbit was eating a carrot.

Victor went home with the trophy and the rabbit. He was glad his big enormous carrot had gone to the fair after all.

Comprehension Check

1. Why was Victor proud of his garden?
2. How did Victor feel when he saw Wiggly eating his carrot?
3. What was on top of Wiggly's trophy?
4. If you were to win a trophy, what would you like it to have written on it?

Skill Check

What is the root word and ending in each of the words below?

hopped   eating   flapped
washed   biggest   cheered
sitting

Solving Problems

People in stories often have problems. The people usually find a way to solve their problems. When you read a story, look for the problem. Then read carefully to see how the problem is solved.

Read the story below.

Ruth had many shoes in her closet. They kept getting mixed up. She had to look and look for two shoes that matched. Finally she found some old shoe boxes. She put one pair of shoes in each box. Whenever she took her shoes off, she put them in a box.

Ruth had a problem. Her shoes kept getting mixed up. How did Ruth solve her problem? Read the story again to find the answer.

Practice

Now read this story.

After class, Julio ran to the coat room. He grabbed a blue coat and started to put it on. "This is not my coat," he said. "It is too small." He remembered that the new boy, Michael, had a blue coat too. Julio ran out to the playground. "Michael, I think you're wearing my coat!" he yelled. Then Julio and Michael changed coats and played tag.

Try to answer these questions about Julio's problem.

1. What was Julio's problem?
2. How did Julio solve the problem?

Now go on to the next story, "Linda's Invention." Look for a problem in the story. How is the problem solved?

Linda's Invention

by Dina Anastasio

It was a hot day in the city. Linda and her friends were sitting on the stoop in front of an apartment building.

After a while Linda got up, walked to the curb, and looked down.

"This city is a mess," she said. "You can hardly see the street anymore. Before long we won't be able to find the cars, or the people, or even the buildings. This city is really a mess!"

Linda's friends nodded, but said nothing. "Don't you *care*?" Linda asked.

Again, Linda's friends said nothing.

"Well, I care," Linda said. "And I'm going to do something about it. I'm going to invent something that will clean up every piece of garbage on this street."

"Sure," said Luis, yawning.

"It's impossible," said Ann without looking up.

"Great idea," said Diane, trying hard not to laugh.

Linda's friends had heard it all before.
Linda was *always* going to invent something.

When it was hot, Linda was going to invent
a machine that would keep her cool.

When she was sad, Linda was going to invent
a machine that would hug her and make her laugh.

When she had nothing to do, Linda was going
to invent her very own roller coaster.

One day Linda was going to invent a fire
hose that sprayed red-and-white water.

And the next day she was going to invent a
robot that sang "Linda is never wrong, Linda is
never wrong."

But Linda never invented anything.

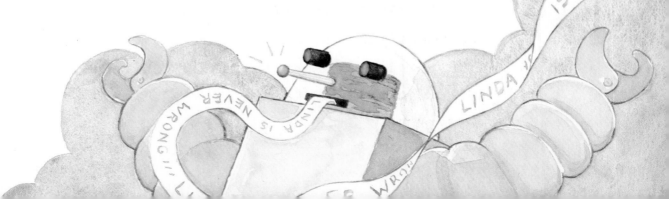

"All right," said Linda. "You just wait!"
And she ran into the apartment building.

Linda did not come out to play the next day,
or the day after that.

"Maybe she's sick," said Luis.

"Maybe she went to her uncle's," said
Ann.

"Maybe she's inventing a machine to clean
up the streets," said Diane. Then everyone
laughed. They all knew that Linda would never
invent anything.

Early the next morning Linda came out of the building. She was carrying a big box. The top of the box had a large hole cut out of it. Above the hole were written the words "THE GARBAGE GAME." Under the hole were the words "TOSS IT IN HERE AND WIN!"

Linda put the box on the sidewalk next to the street. Then she walked back to the stoop and sat down next to her friends.

"What's that?" asked Luis.

"It's my invention," Linda said.

Linda's friends looked at the box and laughed.

"That's silly," said Ann. "How's that going to clean up our street?"

"Just wait," said Linda.

"We'll have to wait for months," laughed Diane.

Linda and her friends sat on the stoop and waited.

At 10 o'clock Luis went upstairs to get an apple. After he had finished eating it, he tossed it into the box.

"That's really a silly game," he said. "It's much too easy. Anybody can hit that hole."

Linda didn't say anything.

124

At 11 a piece of paper floated by. Diane picked it up and tossed it into the box.

"The hole's too big," she said. "It's impossible to miss."

Linda didn't say anything.

At 12 a young boy rode by on his bike. He was peeling a banana. When he saw the box, he stopped and threw the peel into it. Then he said, "What do I win?"

"Look at the clean sidewalk," said Linda.

The boy looked. Then he shrugged and got back on his bike. As he turned the corner, he said, "That's a very silly game."

TOSS IT
IN HERE

The next four people who came by tossed their garbage into the box.

Linda didn't say anything.

But Luis did. "I see," he said. "The hole is supposed to be big. That way no one can miss."

Linda smiled.

"The sidewalk *is* pretty clean," said Ann.

Linda smiled again.

"Not a bad invention," said Diane.

Linda kept right on smiling.

No one said anything for a long time. They
were looking at the sidewalk. Then Luis leaned
back and said, "You know, it's nice."

"Yes," Linda said. "It's very nice."

Comprehension Check

1. Why did Linda want to invent something?
2. Why didn't Ann look up when Linda said she was going to invent something?
3. How do you think Linda felt when her friends thought her invention was silly?
4. Can you think of other ways to clean up city streets? What are they?

Skill Check

1. What was the problem in the story you just read?
2. How did Linda solve the problem?

Stone Soup

Literary Unit

Gold Medal
Selection

by Marcia Brown

Three soldiers walked down the road in a
strange country. They were tired, and they were
hungry. In fact, they had eaten nothing for two
days.

"How I would like a good dinner tonight,"
said the first.

"And a bed to sleep in," said the second.

"But all that is impossible," said the third.
"We must march on."

On they marched. Suddenly they saw the lights of a town.

"Maybe we'll find a bite to eat there," said the first.

"And a bed to sleep in," said the second.

"It can't hurt to ask," said the third.

Now, the people of that town were afraid of strangers. When they heard that three soldiers were coming down the road, they talked among themselves.

"Here come three soldiers. Soldiers are always hungry. But we have little enough food for ourselves." And they hurried to hide their food.

The townspeople pushed sacks of barley under the hay in the lofts. They lowered buckets of milk down the wells.

They spread old quilts over the carrot bins. They hid their cabbages and potatoes under the beds. They hung their meat in the cellars.

They hid all they had to eat. Then they waited.

The soldiers stopped first at the house of Paul and Francoise.

"Good day to you," they said. "Would you have a bit of food for three hungry soldiers?"

"We've had no food for ourselves for three days," said Paul. "It has been a bad year."

The three soldiers went on to the house of Albert and Louise.

"Would you have a bit of food?"

"Oh, no," said Albert. "We gave all our food to soldiers who came before you."

It was the same everywhere the soldiers went. No one had any food to give away.

The people stood in the street and stared.

The three soldiers talked together.

Then the first soldier called out, "Good people!" The people moved closer.

"We are three hungry soldiers in a strange land. We have asked you for food, and you have no food. Well then, we'll have to make stone soup."

The people stared.

Stone soup? That would be something to know about.

"First we'll need a large pot," the soldiers said.

The people brought the largest pot they could find. How else would the soldiers be able to cook enough?

"And now we need water to fill the pot and a fire to heat it," said the soldiers.

It took many buckets of water to fill the pot. A fire was built on the town square and the pot was set on it.

"And now, if you please," the soldiers said, "we need three smooth stones."

Those were easy enough to find.

The people's eyes grew round as they watched the soldiers put the stones into the pot.

134

"And soup needs salt and pepper," said the soldiers.

The town's children ran to get salt and pepper.

"Most of the time stones make good soup. But oh, if there were carrots, it would be much better," the soldiers said.

"Why, I think I have a carrot or two," said Francoise, and off she ran.

She came back with her apron full of carrots from the bin under the old quilt.

"A good stone soup should have cabbage,"
said the soldiers.

"I think I could find a cabbage somewhere,"
said Marie. She came back with three cabbages
from the cupboard under the bed.

"If we only had a bit of meat and a few
potatoes, this soup would be good enough for
a rich person's table," said the soldiers.

A rich person's soup! All from a few
stones. It seemed like magic.

"Now," sighed the soldiers as they stirred in the meat and potatoes, "if we only had a little barley and a cup of milk! This soup would be fit for the king himself. As a matter of fact, he asked for just such a soup the last time we ate with him."

The people looked at each other. The soldiers had eaten with the king himself! Well!

The people brought their barley. They brought their milk.

And at last the soup was ready.

Such a soup! How good it smelled!

But then the people asked themselves, "Would not such a soup need bread and a roast beef?" Soon the table was full and everyone sat down to eat.

Never had there been such a feast. Never had the people eaten such a soup. And just think, the soup was made from stones!

The people ate and ate. And after that they danced and sang. They danced and sang far into the night.

At last they were tired. Then the three
soldiers asked, "Is there not a loft where we
could sleep?"

"Let three such wise and important men sleep
in a loft? Never! They must have the best beds
in the town," said the people.

So the first soldier slept in the butcher's
house.

The second soldier slept in the baker's
house.

And the third soldier slept in the mayor's
house.

In the morning the whole town gathered in
the square to give the soldiers a send-off.

"Many thanks for what you have taught us,"
the people said. "We shall never go hungry now
that we know how to make soup from stones."

"Oh, it's all in knowing how," said the
soldiers. Then off they went down the road.

140

SECTION TWO

The Flying Patchwork Quilt

by Barbara Brenner

If it weren't for my mom, it would never have happened.

You see, my mom goes to antique shops, and she buys old things. Then she puts them around the house.

Well, one day my mom came home with an old pine chest. "It will be a perfect place to store winter things," she told my dad. "And look what's at the bottom of it."

"What is it?" asked my dad.

"It's a piece of an old patchwork quilt," my mom said. "Isn't it pretty?"

142

She held it up, and we all came around to take a look. It was small—only about as big as a beach towel. And it was old—very old. But bright! It was just about the most rainbow-colored thing I'd ever seen.

"It is pretty," my dad said, "but what are you going to do with it?"

"I'll think of something," my mom said. She folded it and put it away in the bottom of the chest.

That was the last I saw of the patchwork quilt for a long time. It lay at the bottom of the old pine chest, and when spring came it got covered with our winter things. Then one day—

my sister, Ellen, and I were out in the backyard. My mom came out. "Carl," she said to me, "I have to do a little shopping. Promise you'll keep an eye on Ellen?"

"I promise," I said. "Don't worry about a thing."

Ellen was playing that flying game she always plays. She was jumping off the bottom porch step.

I looked over once in a while. I watched her jump and land.

I looked up again. There was Ellen, about to try flying with the old patchwork quilt! "No, you don't," I cried. "That's Mom's."

144

"Please, Carl," she said. "I just want to try it."

"All right. But promise that after you fall down with that silly thing you will stop playing this game for the rest of the day!"

She promised.

I helped her pin it around her. When she stood on the porch steps, I moved back so she could make her jump.

"One, two, three!" she shouted.

"Jump," I said.

She did.

Now, I'm not making this up. One minute she
was jumping off the porch steps. The next minute
she was floating over my head. There she was,
with her sneakers in my face.

"I told you, I told you!" she kept shouting
as she flew above my head. "I knew the
patchwork quilt was the right thing."

The wind tossed her up a little higher. She
began to look a bit scared.

"Carl?" she called, kind of funny.

The wind blew harder. She went higher and
higher and then right over the house. Before I
knew it, the wind was blowing her away.

"Don't worry! I'm coming," I shouted as I
climbed onto my bike. By the time I started
down the driveway, I could hardly see her.

I was almost at Cassebeer's Flower Farm when
I thought I saw something. Something seemed to
be floating above the flowers. So I left my bike
and began to run up and down the rows.

As I came to the last row of flowers, I
looked out over the lake.

There she was!

She was doing something that looked like water-skiing without water skis. Her sneakers were pretty wet, and she looked really scared.

"Try to turn," I called to her. "Put the quilt around your arms. Flap your left arm and you'll go to the right. Flap your right arm and you'll go to the left."

"Which is left?" she called back.

"Flap them both," I said.

She did. Slowly she began to move away from the water.

As soon as she was over land, the wind took her higher again.

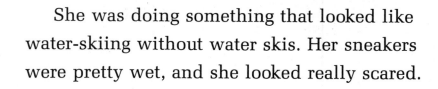

I climbed back on my bike again and began
to ride. I rode past the creek and past the library.
As I rode by, I looked up.

And there was Ellen. Right smack on top of
the library flagpole. Boy, was I glad to see her!

"Don't worry," I cried. "Help is on the way."

I ran into the library.

"Mrs. Lojahn," I shouted. "My sister's been
flying all over town and now she's STUCK on the
flagpole."

We ran out of the library. Mrs. Lojahn
looked up to the top of the flagpole. I looked
up too.

Ellen wasn't there.

There was nothing to say. I just turned away,
climbed on my bike, and rode off.

Might as well go home.

Literary Unit

When I rode into the driveway, I could hardly believe my eyes. But sure enough, there was Ellen. She was sitting in the tree at the far end of the yard.

"Where have you been?" I shouted.

"I couldn't help it, Carl," she said. "The patchwork quilt *made* me do it. I was really scared. But it was fun too. And now I'm stuck in this tree."

I helped her down. Then I folded the quilt and raced to my room.

That night I could hardly wait for everyone to go to bed.

I stood by the window for a long time, looking up into the dark night sky.

Then I picked up the quilt and put it around me. "Well, here goes!" I said.

But the pin was gone. I put the quilt down and turned to get another pin.

In that second it happened. The wind picked up the quilt and blew it out into the night.

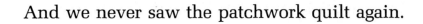

And we never saw the patchwork quilt again.

I'd think I dreamed it all if it weren't for my sister, Ellen. She remembers everything. My mom remembers too, in a way. Every once in a while she says, "I wonder what happened to that pretty little quilt that was in the pine chest?"

Comprehension Check

1. What did Carl's mother buy?
2. How do you think Carl felt when his sister was flying through the air?
3. Why did Carl start to pin the quilt around himself at the end of the story?
4. If you could fly, where would you go?

The Kite

by Harry Behn

How bright on the blue
Is a kite when it's new!

With a dive and a dip
It snaps its tail

Then soars like a ship
With only a sail

As over tides
Of wind it rides,

Then seems to rest
As wind falls.

Possum Was Fooled

by Shirley Patterson

Possum was hanging by his tail from a tree. He couldn't sleep so he was staring at the ground.

Possum thought he saw his friend Snake. Snake seemed to be bent across a stick.

"Are you napping?" asked Possum.

There was no answer.

"Get up, or you'll hurt your back. You're bent in the middle, and that's dangerous," Possum said.

Snake still did not answer.

Possum was worried. He called to Raccoon.

Raccoon popped her head out of the tree.

"Snake is bent," said Possum.

Raccoon leaned out of her nest to look. "No, he's not," she said. "He's just taking a nap."

"He may be napping," answered Possum, "but he's also bent."

"Oh, my," said Raccoon. "That can't be good for his health."

Soon Woodpecker hopped out of the tree. He wanted to see what was happening.

"Snake is bent," Possum said.

"He looks like he's taking a nap," said Woodpecker.

"He may be napping," said Possum, "but he's also bent."

"I *know* that can't be good for his health," said Raccoon.

The three friends decided they'd better do something to help Snake.

Possum said, "Perhaps we can straighten Snake by hanging him from a tree. I find that very nice."

"No," said Woodpecker. "Snake should *not* hang from a tree. It's dangerous."

"And it's *definitely* not good for his health," said Raccoon.

Then Woodpecker said, "I could straighten Snake with a few light taps from my bill."

"No," Possum said. "That's dangerous too. Your bill will hurt him."

"And that would be *very* bad for his health," said Raccoon. "But wait a minute. I have an idea. Let's move him off the stick."

"You might have something there," said Possum. "Moving Snake might be just the thing to do."

Just then the three friends heard Snake calling to them.

"What's the matter?" asked Snake.

Possum and Raccoon and Woodpecker saw Snake moving across the ground under the tree.

"There are *two* of him!" Woodpecker cried. "One is on the stick and the other is on his way here."

"This is not good for *my* health!" said Raccoon.

Snake laughed. "Did you think *I* was stuck on that stick? That's just my old skin."

Snake told his friends that sometimes he shed his old skin after he had grown a new one under it.

"I wonder if that's good for his health?" said Raccoon.

"How do you like that!" said Woodpecker. "It was just his old skin all the time."

"I sure was fooled!" said Possum. Then he went to sleep.

Comprehension Check

1. Why was Possum worried about Snake?
2. Why did Possum want to hang Snake from a tree?
3. Was Woodpecker's idea a good one? Why or why not?
4. Have you ever seen an interesting animal? What was it?

Skill Check

What is the root word and ending in each of the words below?

staring   napping   popped
straighten   taking   decided

Order in a Story

Many things happen in order. First you put on your socks. Then you put on your shoes. First you open a door. Then you go through the door. Things happen in order in stories too. A story makes more sense when you can tell what happens first, next, and last.

Read this story.

The bear wanted a place to sleep for the winter. First she found a cave. Next she made a bed of leaves and branches. Finally she curled up and went to sleep for a long time.

Can you tell what happened first in the story you just read? If you said that the bear found a cave, you were right. What is the last thing the bear did? Look at the last sentence of the story. The bear curled up and went to sleep.

Practice

Now read this story.

Larry and Betty made peanut-butter sandwiches. First they put pieces of bread on a plate. Next they opened the jar of peanut butter. Finally they put peanut butter on the bread.

In what order did things happen in the story? Answer the questions below.

1. What did Larry and Betty do first?

   a. They opened the jar of peanut butter.

   b. They put pieces of bread on a plate.

2. What did Larry and Betty do next?

   a. They put the peanut butter on the bread.

   b. They opened the jar of peanut butter.

3. What did Larry and Betty do last?

   a. They put peanut butter on the bread.

   b. They put pieces of bread on the plate.

As you read "The Magpie's Nest," pay attention to the order in which things happen.

The Magpie's Nest

adapted from an English folk tale

The Players

NARRATOR   BLACKBIRD

PERSON IN AUDIENCE   WISE OWL

MAGPIE   STARLING

THRUSH   TURTLE DOVE

NARRATOR: Good afternoon. (*Steps up and bows.*)
Have you ever wondered why some birds
build their nests one way and other
birds build their nests another way?

PERSON IN AUDIENCE (*shouting*): No.

NARRATOR: Well, I am going to tell you anyway.

PERSON IN AUDIENCE: Why?

NARRATOR: Because it's a very interesting
story. Now I will begin.
(*MAGPIE comes in and sits at the side
of the stage.*)

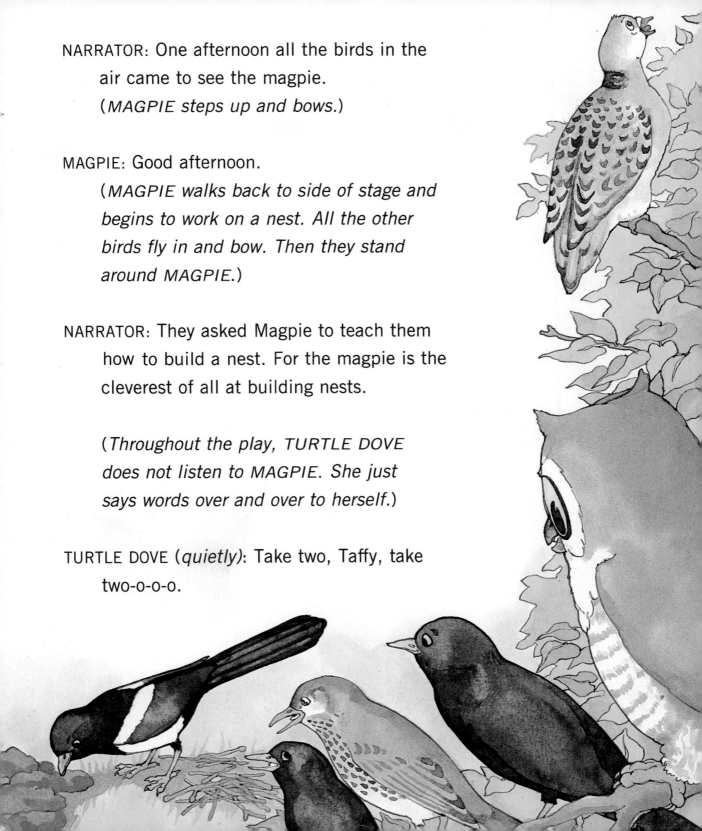

NARRATOR: One afternoon all the birds in the
air came to see the magpie.
(*MAGPIE steps up and bows.*)

MAGPIE: Good afternoon.
(*MAGPIE walks back to side of stage and
begins to work on a nest. All the other
birds fly in and bow. Then they stand
around MAGPIE.*)

NARRATOR: They asked Magpie to teach them
how to build a nest. For the magpie is the
cleverest of all at building nests.

(*Throughout the play, TURTLE DOVE
does not listen to MAGPIE. She just
says words over and over to herself.*)

TURTLE DOVE (*quietly*): Take two, Taffy, take
two-o-o-o.

MAGPIE: To begin, you must take some mud and make a sort of round cake with it.

THRUSH: Oh, I see how it is done. That will be very simple.

NARRATOR: . . . said the thrush. And the thrush flew away before the magpie could finish. (*The thrush flies away.*)

PERSON IN AUDIENCE: Then how did the thrush build her nest?

NARRATOR: She built it out of mud. That's all. Nothing more. And that is how thrushes build their nests to this very day.

MAGPIE: Let's finish the nest. Next you must
find some twigs and put them in the mud.

BLACKBIRD: Oh, how interesting. Now I see.

NARRATOR: . . . said the blackbird. (*The
blackbird flies away.*) And she flew
away. And that is how blackbirds
build their nests.

PERSON IN AUDIENCE: Do they really build them that way?

NARRATOR: Yes, they really do.

MAGPIE: And now you must put more mud over the twigs.

WISE OWL: Oh, I knew that all along.

NARRATOR: . . . said the wise owl. (*The wise owl flies away.*) And she flew away. And that is why owls have never made better nests since then.

168

MAGPIE: Next you must tie more twigs around the outside. And you will need some feathers and other things to line the nest. That will make it nice and comfortable.

STARLING: That sounds simple.

NARRATOR: . . . said the starling. (*The starling flies away.*) And she flew away to begin her nest. And now a starling's nest is always nice and comfortable.

PERSON IN AUDIENCE: I guess the starling was the only one who stayed around long enough.

NARRATOR: Not really. The magpie wasn't quite finished.

NARRATOR: All the birds stayed around long
enough to learn something about
building a nest. But no one stayed
around long enough to learn everything.
And that is why different birds build
their nests in different ways.
(*All the birds are gone except TURTLE
DOVE.*)

PERSON IN AUDIENCE: Wait! The turtle dove is
still there.

NARRATOR: I know. But the turtle dove wasn't
listening.

TURTLE DOVE (*loudly*): Take two, Taffy, take
two-o-o-o.

MAGPIE (*putting a twig on the nest*): One more
   twig is enough.

TURTLE DOVE: Take two, Taffy, take two-o-o-o.

MAGPIE (*angrily*): One twig is enough, I tell
   you!

TURTLE DOVE: Take two, Taffy, take two-o-o-o.

NARRATOR: The magpie became very angry and
   flew away. (*The magpie flies away.*)

PERSON IN AUDIENCE: That was a very
   interesting story.

NARRATOR: I told you it would be. (*Bows and
   walks off.*)

Comprehension Check

1. Why did the other birds ask Magpie to teach them how to build nests?
2. Why did the birds in the play build different kinds of nests?
3. Do you think that the turtle dove learned how to build a nest? Why or why not?
4. Have you ever tried to explain something to someone who wasn't listening? How did you get the person to listen?

Skill Check

1. What was the first thing that Magpie did when she was building the nest?
2. What was the second thing that Magpie did when she was building the nest?
3. What was the third thing that Magpie did when she was building the nest?

QUBE TV

by Howard Lavine

Color the Clown

The woman on the television set held up a picture of a clown. The picture was from a coloring book.

"This is Mr. Clown," she said. "I'm afraid he isn't very interesting. I think he needs a little color. Do you agree?"

Kiyo was watching her TV at home. "I agree," she thought.

The woman went on. "Let's begin with his eyes. What color do you think I should make them? If you think Mr. Clown's eyes should be blue, push button number one. If you think they should be brown, push number two. And if you think they should be green, push number three."

Kiyo thought about her brother. His eyes were brown. They were nice. Kiyo looked at the buttons on the special TV box in her lap. Then she pushed button number two.

"Most of you want brown," the woman on the TV said. "I'm going to color the clown's eyes dark, dark brown. OK. What about his hair?

If you think it should be brown, push button number one. If you think it should be black, push button two. If you think it should be blond, push three. And if you think it should be red, push four."

This time Kiyo pushed number four.

"Most of you agree that the clown's hair should be red," the woman said.

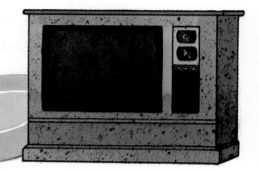

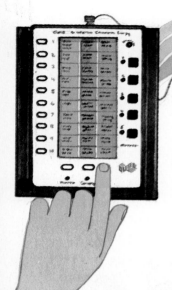

What Is QUBE TV?

Could the story that you just read really happen? Can you tell a person on television just what you think?

If you live in Columbus, Ohio, you would be able to tell the people at a television station how you feel. All you have to do is push a button. The people in this city are trying out a new kind of television called QUBE TV.

QUBE TV is a lot like a telephone. When you use a telephone, you send a message to the person you are calling. QUBE TV works the same way. You use a special box that comes with the TV. When you push a button, you send a message to the people at the television station. The buttons mean different things at different times. A button can stand for eye color, or hair color, or almost anything else.

176

QUBE TV Games

Here are some of the games that have been played on QUBE TV. They are very much like games you've already seen on television. But with QUBE TV the children watching at home play too.

The Spelling Game is one of the shows. There are two teams of children in the television studio. One is the red team. The other is the blue team. Half the children watching at home are on the red team. The other half are on the blue team.

Kiyo is on the blue team. As she watches, five words appear on the television screen.

"All right, blue team," the woman on the TV says to the children at home. "Look at these words. Then choose one that you would like the red team here in the studio to spell."

Kiyo decides that word number two is the hardest. She pushes that button.

All over Columbus other players on the blue team are pushing a button too.

Word number three appears on the screen.

"Most of the blue team agrees on this word," the woman says. Kiyo is sorry. She thinks the word is too easy. And she is right. In the studio someone on the red team spells the word correctly, and Kiyo's team loses.

Television in the Future

QUBE TV shows tell us what TV might be like in the future. Today you don't have much to say about what you see on television. But someday you might.

One day someone will appear on your screen and say, "We've been showing you the Spelling Game for a long time now. We are thinking of taking it off the air. If you would like to see something else, push button number one. If not, push button two."

Will QUBE TV ever come to your house? Many people think so. How long will it take? No one knows for sure. But Kiyo hopes that it will be very soon.

"It would be nice to have more people on the blue team," she says. "Just think, if children all over the United States had been playing the Spelling Game, our team might have won."

Comprehension Check

1. Why did Kiyo want the clown's eyes to be brown?
2. Why did the woman in the television studio color the clown's hair red?
3. What do you think you would like about QUBE TV?
4. In what other ways might QUBE TV be used?

Skill Check

Use the Contents at the front of this book to answer these questions.

1. On what page does the section "Color the Clown" begin?
2. Where would you find the first page of the section about QUBE TV games?
3. If you wanted to read about television in the future, what page would you turn to?

The Mysterious Shadow

by Joan Lowery Nixon

"There's a shadow on the porch," Jonathan said. "I think someone's looking in our window!"

He ran to the window, but the shadow was gone. He opened the door, but no one was on the porch.

"Is anybody there?" Jonathan whispered. No one answered. Jonathan locked the door and sat down next to his father.

"I think someone was looking in our window!" he said in a whisper.

"It was probably the wind," his father said. He was reading the mail. "Here's a card from the people who used to live on the corner. It seems the family who moved into their house has two girls. Anne is fourteen and Pat is your age, Jonathan."

Jonathan hardly listened. He was too busy thinking about the mysterious shadow.

In the morning Jonathan saw a spot in the middle of the window. There were spots on each side of it.

"Fingerprints!" Jonathan said to himself. "And a round noseprint in the middle!"

That day he wore his detective cap to school.
He thought about the shadow all day long.

After school someone knocked softly at his
front door. Jonathan waited. The person knocked
again, louder this time. Jonathan ran to the
door. But when he opened it, no one was there.

Jonathan ran outside and looked up and down
the street.

"Come back here, mysterious shadow!" he
shouted.

But he was too late. No one was in the
street. The mysterious shadow was gone.

There was a strange mark on the sidewalk.

"Hmmm," Jonathan said to himself. "A bicycle mark! It seems someone has been riding a bicycle through the wet grass and has left a mark on the sidewalk. So! The mysterious shadow rides a bicycle!"

Jonathan went upstairs and got his magnifying glass. Then he went outside again. He looked at the mark for a long time.

"Hmmm," he said at last. "It seems one tire has a patch on it."

Literary Unit

At school the next day Jonathan told his friend about the mysterious shadow.

"This is what I know so far," he said. "First, the shadow makes round noseprints. And second, the shadow rides a bicycle with a patch on one tire."

"It's probably a cat or something," his friend said as he ran off to play ball.

"Anyone knows a cat can't ride a bicycle!" Jonathan shouted after him.

After school Jonathan went to the playground and tossed a ball around. He hoped people would think he was just playing ball. What he was really doing was searching for the mysterious shadow.

Then he had an idea.

There were many bicycles at the playground. If he searched through all of them, he might find a tire with a patch on it.

Jonathan tossed the ball aside and went to work.

Jonathan searched for a long time. And then he found it. The bicycle was bright blue.

Jonathan waited behind a big tree, watching to see who would come for the bicycle.

In a few minutes a boy took the bicycle and rode away. Jonathan had never seen the boy before.

Jonathan raced after the boy.

The boy turned at the corner. Jonathan followed.

The boy turned again at the next corner. Jonathan still followed. He was getting tired.

"Hey!" thought Jonathan. "This is *my* street!"

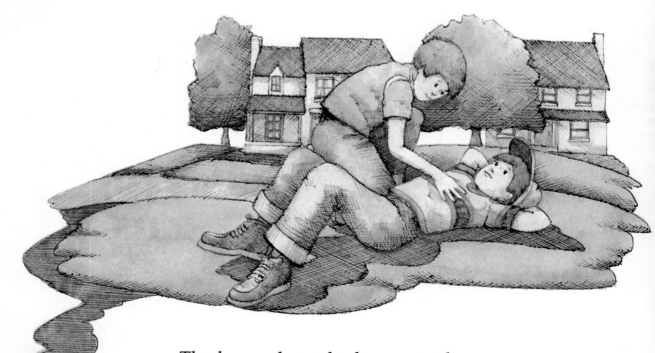

The boy rode to the house on the corner.
Jonathan was so tired he fell on the grass.
The boy came and sat next to him.

"Are you all right?" he asked.

"I guess," Jonathan whispered, "but I didn't
know *anybody* could ride that fast."

He looked at the house.

"Hey," he asked, "do you live here too? Do
you have a sister named Anne and a sister named
Pat?"

190

"No," the boy said. "My name is Pat—Patrick—and I know your name. I came to your house to meet you. Once I looked in your window. Once I knocked on your door. But I was too scared to say hello. I'm kind of a shy person."

"So it was *you*!" Jonathan said.

Jonathan thought for a minute. "Come over to my house," he said, "and I'll tell you a funny story about a mysterious shadow."

Comprehension Check

1. What did Jonathan see on the porch?
2. Who left fingerprints on Jonathan's window?
3. Do you think it was a good idea to search for a patch on the bicycle tires? Why?
4. Have you ever solved a mystery? What was it?

To be read by the teacher

Poem

I loved my friend.
He went away from me.
There's nothing more to say.
The poem ends,
Soft as it began—
I loved my friend.

Langston Hughes

192

Which Things Go Together?

You can put things together in groups because they are alike. They may be the same color, shape, or size. They may also do the same job or be used the same way.

Read the story below.

Paco was cleaning the kitchen. He put the vegetables in the refrigerator and the dishes on the shelf.

Look at the pictures below. Tell which things are <u>vegetables</u> that belong in the refrigerator. Tell which things are <u>dishes</u> that belong on the shelf.

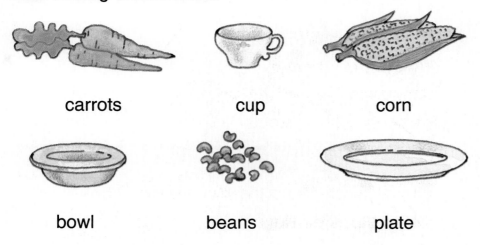

carrots   cup   corn

bowl   beans   plate

The carrots, the corn, and the beans are
vegetables. Paco should put them in the
refrigerator. The cup, the bowl, and the plate
are dishes. Paco should put them on the shelf.

Practice

Read the following paragraph.

Paco went for a walk after he cleaned
the kitchen. As he walked, he saw some
things on the street and some things in
the air.

The things Paco saw are in the pictures
below. Tell which things Paco saw in the
air. Tell which things Paco saw on the ground.

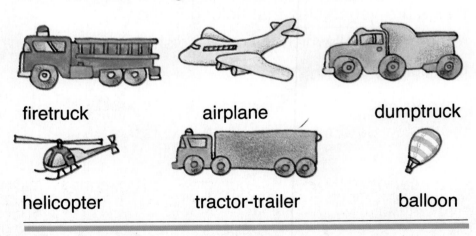

firetruck   airplane   dumptruck

helicopter   tractor-trailer   balloon

As you read "Mario the Magnificient," look
for things that are alike.

Mario the Magnificent

by Kevin Johnson

The Players

MARIO LITTLE BROTHER

SHOPKEEPERS WOMAN

(*SHOPKEEPERS stand side by side. Each is holding a sign. MARIO is walking back and forth in front of the signs. LITTLE BROTHER is following him.*)

MARIO: I am Mario the Magnificent, the world's greatest problem solver. (*Stops and shakes his head. LITTLE BROTHER does the same.*) But today is a very bad day, for the great Mario does not have a problem to solve.

WOMAN (*taps MARIO on the shoulder and hands him an envelope*): Did you drop this? (*MARIO looks in envelope.*)

MARIO: Hmmm. It's a twenty-dollar bill. Wait a minute, there's a note here.

LITTLE BROTHER: What does it say?

MARIO: I can only read part of it. Some of the words are missing. Water must have washed away some of the ink. (*Reads note.*)

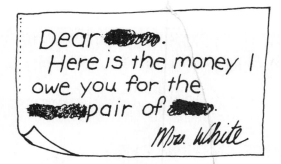

MARIO (*walking back and forth. LITTLE BROTHER is following.*): Another problem for Mario the Magnificent.

LITTLE BROTHER: And his smart little brother.

MARIO (*ignoring him*): I must return this money at once. But I don't know who should get it.

LITTLE BROTHER: Give it to the person who sold Mrs. White a pair of something.

MARIO (*ignoring him*): I know! I'll return it to the person who sold Mrs. White a pair of something!

LITTLE BROTHER: Good idea.

MARIO (*stopping in front of clothing store*):
Hmmm, I wonder if anything in a clothing
store comes in pairs? Let's see, a pair
of hats? A pair of coats?

LITTLE BROTHER: That's silly. How about a pair
of pants, a pair of socks, a pair of
gloves, a pair of . . .

MARIO: All right. All right. (*Knocks on sign.
Person holding sign lowers it and becomes
SHOPKEEPER. She reads note, then shakes
her head. MARIO and LITTLE BROTHER walk
on.*)

(*MARIO and LITTLE BROTHER stop in front of shoe store.*)

MARIO: Hmmm, I wonder if a shoe store has a
pair of anything.

LITTLE BROTHER: A pair of boots, a pair of
sneakers, a pair of shoes, a pair of . . .

(*MARIO puts his hand over LITTLE
BROTHER's mouth. Then he knocks on sign.
The person holding the sign lowers it. The person
reads the note, shakes his head, and hands
envelope to LITTLE BROTHER.*)

MR. FIX-IT'S CAR REPAIR

We Fix Trucks

We Fix Cars

(*LITTLE BROTHER stops in front of car repair shop and looks at the sign. He opens the note and reads it.*)

LITTLE BROTHER (*reading*): "Here is the money I owe you for the _____ pair of_____." I know! It's not a pair of anything!

MARIO: Maybe it's a pair of lions.

(*LITTLE BROTHER knocks on the "Car Repair" sign. SHOPKEEPER lowers his sign and reads the note.*)

SHOPKEEPER: The money's mine, all right. Mrs. White was bringing it here when she lost it. I fixed her car. The note should say: "Here is the money I owe you for the *repair* of my car." (*He shakes their hands and raises sign.*)

MARIO (*bowing*): Mario the Magnificent does it again! (*He walks off. LITTLE BROTHER follows.*)

200

Comprehension Check

1. Why couldn't Mario read all of the words on the note?
2. Why did Mario and his little brother think that Mrs. White had bought a pair of something?
3. Which brother do you think was smarter?
4. What other things could Mario and his brother have done to solve the problem in the story?

Skill Check

1. Can you name three things that are sold in a clothing store?
2. What were some of the things that were sold in the shoe shop?
3. What other things can you think of that come in pairs?

The New Girl in School

by Judy Delton

My mother got a new job today. I got a new school.

"It will be fun," said my mother. "You will meet lots of new friends there."

When I walked in, everybody stared. Everybody was friends with each other but me.

I wore my new dress with the octopus on it. (No one cared.)

The teacher called me Martha. (My name is Marcia.)

Everyone had a ball-point pen. (I had a pencil.)

Everyone understood subtraction. (Except me.)

"I don't like this school," I told my mother that night.

"It will be better tomorrow," she said.

SCHOOL DISTRICT

The next day I sat alone on the bus. (The seats were for two.)

In line I was the only one without a partner. Everyone pushed. (I hurt my knee.)

"Today was no better," I said to my mother that night. "I don't like being the new girl in school."

"Tomorrow is another day," said my mother.

On Wednesday I didn't want to go to school. I cried and said I had the mumps. I cried and said I'd run away. My mother said, "Get on the bus."

At school we drew pictures. The teacher held the best pictures up in front of the class. (My picture wasn't one of them.)

We played Captain-May-I? (I wasn't the captain.)

But when we played baseball, I made it to second base.

That night my mother said, "How was school?"

"Give it time," I said.

"Maybe I should talk to the teacher tomorrow," she said.

"I'm not a baby," I said.

On Thursday we made airplanes, and the teacher hung mine up. (Just mine.)

I wore my octopus dress and someone said, "Is that a snake?"

I said, "No, it's an octopus."

Karen asked me to her birthday party. (She could only ask eight.)

On Friday my mother said, "You *could* stay with Grandma, and go to your old school."

"Why?" I said. "I'm used to this one now. And guess what? There was a new girl at school today. And she doesn't understand subtraction."

Comprehension Check

1. Why did Marcia cry and say she had the mumps?
2. On page 204, why did Marcia say, "Today was no better"?
3. Do you think Marcia gave the school a chance before she decided she didn't like it? Why or why not?
4. How would you help a new person in school to feel at home?

Skill Check

1. Find the word *there* on page 202. To what place does *there* refer?
2. Find the word *I* on page 203. To which person does *I* refer?
3. Find the word *she* at the bottom of page 206. To which person does *she* refer?

Feelings in a Story

Sometimes there are words in a story to tell you how a person feels. You can also guess how a person in a story feels by what the person says or does. Read the paragraphs below.

Kito was sad. His best friend, Harold, had moved to a new neighborhood. "I'm lonely without my friend," Kito said. He sat quietly on the steps of his house.

One day Harold's father came to visit Kito's father. Harold came too. Kito was happy. "I'm glad to see you, Harold," Kito said. He and Harold talked and played together all afternoon.

1. What word in the beginning of the story tells you how Kito felt?

2. What did Kito say and do at the beginning of the story that tells how he felt?

3. What word tells how Kito felt when Harold came to visit?

4. What did Kito say and do then that tells how he felt?

Practice

In the next story look for words that tell how Marsha feels. Look for things that Marsha says and does that tell how she feels.

Marsha was angry. Her sister had borrowed her pen and forgotten to return it. "I'm really mad at you," Marsha said to Nina. She gave Nina a mean look.

"I used your pen to write you a birthday card," said Nina. "Surprise!"

Marsha was suddenly happy. "I'm glad you remembered my birthday." Marsha smiled. "But I would like my pen back."

1. What word in the beginning of the story tells you how Marsha felt?

2. What did Marsha say and do in the beginning of the story that tells how she felt?

3. What word tells how Marsha felt when Nina told her why she took the pen?

4. What did Marsha say and do then that showed how she felt?

Read the next story about a cat who runs away. Notice the words that tell how the cats and their owner feel.

Millie Ran Away

by Dina Anastasio

When Millie ran away, I didn't really
worry. She had run away before, lots of times.
But she always came back.

This time it was different. A week went
by. Then two weeks went by. Millie still
didn't return. I missed her very much.

Every morning, before I went to school,
I went out to the woods behind our house
and called her.

"Here, Millie. Here, Millie."

But she never answered.

One day, when Millie had been gone for six
weeks, my mother said, "Would you like to get
a kitten?"

"What if Millie comes home?" I said. "What
if Millie comes home and finds a kitten at the
foot of my bed?"

"I don't think Millie is coming home," my
mother said. "Six weeks is a long time."

I thought about what she had said. Then I
said, "I guess it will be all right." But I
wasn't really sure.

Later I went out to the woods to call Millie one last time.

The next day my mother brought home a kitten. She was gray and white, and she looked like a mouse.

"Hello, Miss Mouse," I said.

That night Miss Mouse slept in my bed, way under the covers. I guess she was scared because she was in a new place. All night she cuddled closer and closer to me. I didn't sleep much, because I was afraid I might roll over and hurt her.

The next day my mother put an old quilt on the kitchen floor and put the kitten on it. That night Miss Mouse slept on the kitchen floor. But in the daytime she slept at the foot of my bed.

And then Millie came home.

We were eating dinner and we heard her crying.

She looked different, bigger somehow, and kind of mean. I guess it was because she had lived on her own for such a long time.

When I opened the door, she ran in and headed straight for the foot of my bed.

And then she saw Miss Mouse.

Miss Mouse seemed happy to see Millie. Maybe she thought that Millie was her mother.

But Millie didn't like Miss Mouse at all. She hissed, backed off, and hissed again.

It went on like that for a while. Miss Mouse tried to cuddle Millie as if she were her mother. And Millie hissed at her. I guess Millie wanted us all to know that she didn't like the idea of someone taking her place.

As the weeks went by, Millie began to change. She still didn't like Miss Mouse very much, but she did stop hissing.

And then one dark morning I went into the kitchen very early. I leaned down to say good morning to Miss Mouse, but I couldn't see her.

Millie was in Miss Mouse's place on the floor. I leaned closer and looked again.

Miss Mouse was there too, sleeping beside Millie. They weren't cuddled close together. But they weren't far apart.

Millie and Miss Mouse get along now. They aren't the best of friends, and I guess they never will be.

So I have two cats now. I wish it hadn't happened quite the way it did, with Millie running away like that. But it's nice to have them just the same.

Comprehension Check

1. Why wasn't Millie's owner worried when Millie ran away?

2. When Millie came home, why did she hiss at Miss Mouse?

3. Do you think that the family in the story should have gotten the kitten? Why or why not?

4. What else could the family in the story have done to find Millie?

Skill Check

1. In the beginning of the story Millie had been gone for two weeks. What words tell you how her owner felt?

2. How did Millie show that she didn't like Miss Mouse?

3. How can you tell that Millie and Miss Mouse were learning to get along with each other by the end of the story?

The Magic Spectacles

based upon a story
by Lilian Moore

Little Hoot lived in a tall tree in the woods.
He was a baby owl. In the very next tree lived
Grandfather Owl.

Little Hoot liked to sit and watch old
Grandfather Owl.

"Grandfather Owl is very wise," whispered
Little Hoot.

Day after day Grandfather Owl sat in his tree, looking out at the world through his spectacles.

Day after day the animals of the woods came to see Grandfather Owl.

Mother Raccoon came to ask about her little one. Poor thing! He had a cold.

Grandfather Owl looked down through his spectacles and told her what to do.

Crow came to ask about a scary man who was standing in Farmer Gray's corn.

Grandfather Owl looked down through his spectacles and told Crow not to be scared. It was only a scarecrow.

Day after day Grandfather Owl sat in his tree, looking out at the world through his spectacles.

"How can he be so wise?" thought Little Hoot.

"It must be the spectacles. The spectacles must be magic!"

One afternoon Little Hoot was playing under a tree. He looked up and saw that Grandfather Owl was asleep. Then he saw that the spectacles were slipping, slipping down Grandfather Owl's face.

Down, down, down, until they fell on Little Hoot's head.

"The magic spectacles!" said Little Hoot.
He put them on and flew back to his tree. "Now
I will know everything!" he said.

Soon Woodchuck came by. He wanted to talk to
Grandfather Owl.

"Grandfather Owl is sleeping," whispered
Little Hoot. "Ask me! I'll give you the answer."

"I need a new home," said Woodchuck, "and
I want to know if it is nicer on the other side
of the woods."

Little Hoot looked through the spectacles.
But the spectacles did not help him. He did not
know if it was nicer on the other side of the
woods. So Woodchuck went away.

Soon Brown Bear came by. He wanted to talk to Grandfather Owl.

"Grandfather Owl is sleeping," whispered Little Hoot. "Ask me! I will give you the answer."

"Tell me a new place to look for honey," said Brown Bear. "I have searched and searched."

Little Hoot looked through the spectacles. But the spectacles did not help him.

"I don't know a place," he told Brown Bear. So poor Brown Bear went away.

"These spectacles are not magic," said Little Hoot. "They are not magic at all! They do not help me to know anything at all."

Grandfather Owl was not really sleeping all this time. Now he looked at Little Hoot and said:

> "Spectacles are for seeing
> and not for knowing.
> Knowing comes with
> growing and growing."

"But I wanted to know everything," said Little Hoot. "The way you do!"

"Little Hoot," said Grandfather Owl, "you know everything now that a little owl has to know. When you are a grandfather owl, you will know everything that a grandfather owl has to know. Now may I have my spectacles, please?"

Grandfather Owl put on his spectacles and closed his eyes.

And this time he *really* went to sleep.

Comprehension Check

1. Why couldn't Little Hoot answer Woodchuck?
2. Why do you think Grandfather Owl was so wise?
3. Do you think that Little Hoot should have tried to act like Grandfather Owl? Why or why not?
4. If you could be an expert at something, what would it be?

Fast and Slow

by John Ciardi

The old crow is getting slow.
   The young crow is not.
Of what the young crow does not know
   The old crow knows a lot.

At knowing things the old crow
   Is still the young crow's master.
What does the slow old crow not know?
   —How to go faster.

The young crow flies above, below,
   and rings around the slow old crow.
What does the fast young crow not know?
   —Where to go.

Plants Do Strange Things

by Hedda Nussbaum

Plants That Move

Have you ever seen a plant walk? Of course not. Plants don't walk. They stay in one place. But that doesn't mean that plants don't move. They DO move.

Flowers open and close. Some close in the rain. They open again when the rain stops. Many flowers close up at night and open in the morning. Others open and close at different times.

226

DANDELION

PUMPKIN

You can tell the time by watching the flowers in a garden. Get up early one morning, at about five o'clock. If you can stay awake, you will see some morning glories opening. If you wait until about 8:30, you will see pumpkin flowers close and dandelions open. At 4:00 in the afternoon, four o'clocks will open.

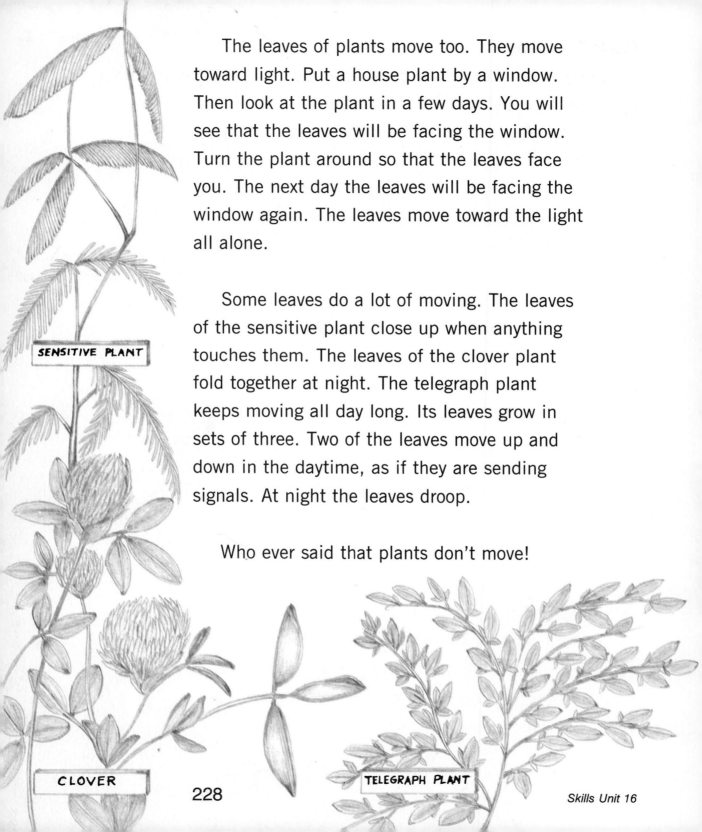

The leaves of plants move too. They move toward light. Put a house plant by a window. Then look at the plant in a few days. You will see that the leaves will be facing the window. Turn the plant around so that the leaves face you. The next day the leaves will be facing the window again. The leaves move toward the light all alone.

Some leaves do a lot of moving. The leaves of the sensitive plant close up when anything touches them. The leaves of the clover plant fold together at night. The telegraph plant keeps moving all day long. Its leaves grow in sets of three. Two of the leaves move up and down in the daytime, as if they are sending signals. At night the leaves droop.

Who ever said that plants don't move!

SENSITIVE PLANT

CLOVER

TELEGRAPH PLANT

228

Plants That Glow

Some plants glow in the dark. They give off light, like little light bulbs. These plants shine in the daylight too. But then we cannot see them.

Some glowing plants shine with a green light. Some shine with an orange light. And some shine with a yellow light.

Which plants glow? Many mushrooms do. Some very small plants that live on old wood do. And many, many plants that live at the bottom of the ocean glow too.

No one knows why these plants glow. Some
scientists think that glowing helps the plants
live. Others say that glowing helped the plants
a long time ago, but that it no longer does.

Would you like to see some plants that glow?
You can sometimes find them in the woods at
night. Look for little patches of pale light
glowing in the dark. The plants' light is
strange and beautiful. People call this light
fox-fire.

Comprehension Check

1. Why do the leaves of a plant lean toward a window?
2. How can you tell the time by watching the flowers in your garden?
3. Why can't you see plants glow in the daylight?
4. What kind of plant would you like to own?

Skill Check

Read the paragraph on page 228 that tells you how a telegraph plant moves. Tell three things about a telegraph plant.

Adding Endings to Words

Letters can be added to the ends of words to make new words. The letters <u>ed</u>, <u>ing</u>, <u>er</u>, <u>est</u>, and <u>en</u> are called **endings.** Words to which endings are added are called **root words**. Sometimes a change is made in a root word before an ending is added.

- The final consonant may be doubled.
  rub + ing = rubbing
- The final <u>e</u> may be dropped.
  smile + ed = smiled
- The final <u>y</u> may be changed to <u>i</u>.
  carry + ed = carried

Read each sentence.
1. Kangaroo was <u>riding</u> the bus to town.
2. She suddenly knew that she had <u>forgotten</u> her money.
3. She <u>worried</u> all the way to the store.
4. In her pockets Kangaroo found some <u>hidden</u> coins.
5. She bought the <u>biggest</u> carrots in the store.

Now look again at each underlined word. What is the root word? What ending was added to the word? How did the word change when the ending was added?

The root words are ride, forgot, worry, hid, and big. The final consonant was doubled in forgotten, hidden, and biggest. The e was dropped in riding. The y was changed to i in worried.

Practice

Now read this story.

Kangaroo waved good-by to the bus driver. She was walking to her house when she saw the funniest thing. Her friend Pig had stopped by to see her. Pig was always messier than anyone else. This time Pig had cooked some soup for Kangaroo, but he tripped on Kangaroo's doorstep. He dropped the soup all over himself. Poor Pig! Kangaroo helped him get cleaned up. Then she shared her carrots with him.

Look again at the underlined words. What is the root word for each one? Which words didn't change when the ending was added? Tell how the other words changed when the ending was added.

Now read the next story about a duck and a bear. If you see a word you don't know, look at the ending of the word. You may know the root word and the ending.

Two Good Friends

by Judy Delton

Duck had cleaned his house. He was looking
at his nice clean rooms. Then he heard a knock
at the door. It was Bear. "Come in," said Duck.
"But wipe your feet."

Bear wiped his feet. Then he went inside, sat
down, and placed his feet on Duck's table. Duck
grabbed a piece of paper and put it under Bear's
feet.

"What do you have to eat?" asked Bear.

"Probably nothing," said Duck. "Today I cleaned my house. I did not bake."

"I have something," said Bear. He reached into his pocket and took out two little honey cakes.

"Bear," cried Duck, "you are spilling crumbs on my floor." He grabbed another piece of paper and put it under Bear's chair.

"Duck," Bear said, "you are a very good housekeeper, but what good is a clean house if you have nothing to eat? Taste one of my honey cakes."

Bear and Duck each ate a honey cake. They spent the rest of the afternoon doing a puzzle.

236

The next day Duck went to see Bear.

"What smells so good?" asked Duck.

"I've been baking," said Bear. He pointed
to a honey cake and some raisin bread. "Brush
the flour off a chair and sit down."

"Bear," said Duck, "I can't sit down. My
foot is stuck."

"Oh, my," said Bear. "That's the honey. Would
you like a piece of honey cake or a piece of
raisin bread?"

"Some raisin bread, please." Duck had
finally gotten his foot unstuck. "I've had enough
honey for one day."

Bear cut one piece of raisin bread for each of them.

"May I have a dish?" asked Duck.

"The dishes are dirty," said Bear.

"Then may I have a fork?" asked Duck.

"The forks are dirty too," said Bear. "I'm sorry. Today I baked, so I didn't have time to wash the dishes. Maybe you can use your wings. The bread will taste good."

When Duck finished, he said, "Bear, you may not be a very good housekeeper, but your raisin bread is the best I have ever tasted."

The next day Bear went to Duck's house with
a surprise. Duck was not at home, but Bear went
inside anyway.

He put six little honey cakes on the table.
Then he wrote a note that said, "From Bear."
After that he went home.

When Bear walked into his house, he was
surprised. "I must be in the wrong house," he
thought. His feet did not stick to the floor.
The dishes were washed. There wasn't a dirty
spot anywhere.

Then he saw a note: "From Duck."

"I must thank Duck," thought Bear.

Just then there was a knock on the door. It was Duck.

"Thank you for the cakes," said Duck. "I was so surprised. And it's not even my birthday."

"And I have never seen my house so clean," said Bear. "I was surprised too."

"We really are good friends," said Duck.

"Yes!" cried Bear. "Now come in and have some raisin bread. But first wipe your feet."

Comprehension Check

1. What does Duck do well?

2. How did Duck use his wings on page 238?

3. Is Duck a neat person? Why do you think as you do?

4. What do you like about Duck? What do you like about Bear?

Skill Check

Look at the words below. They are from the story. What is the root word for each one? What ending was added to each root word?

wiped   baking   cried

placed   grabbed   baked

tasted

How to Give a Magic Show

by Rose Wyler and Gerald Ames

To give a magic show, you will need a ruler, a rubber band, a hat, a ribbon, two pennies, a plate, and a piece of paper. Now you are ready to begin. To start your magic show, wave the ruler and say, "This is a real magic wand. It can move by itself." Push the ruler into your closed hand. Then hold up your hand and the ruler will begin to move. It will slowly rise from your hand.

242

How the Trick Is Done

Slip a rubber band over your finger. Stretch the rubber band over the bottom of the ruler. The rubber band stretches as you push the ruler down. Then the rubber band pulls the ruler up.

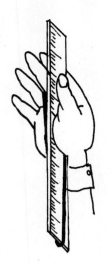

Surprise from a Hat

To do your next trick, put the hat on a table right side up. Then lift the hat up and say, "Does anybody know what is under this hat?"

Everyone will agree that there is nothing under it.

Now turn the hat over and put it back on the table. Then wave your wand over the hat, reach into it, and pull out—a long ribbon.

How the Trick Is Done

Put a roll of ribbon under the band inside the hat. It will stay there when the hat is right side up. But when the hat is turned over, the roll will slip down. Then you can take hold of the end and pull the ribbon out.

244

Drop a Penny Through a Plate

The next trick has four steps.

First say "The next trick is done with a penny."

Next wrap a penny in a piece of paper, put it on a small plate, and set the plate on a glass. Then pick up the magic wand and wave it over the plate. Go on by tapping the plate again and again until—the penny drops right through the plate and falls into the glass!

Does the penny really drop through the plate? Shake out the paper and show your friends that it is indeed empty.

How the Trick Is Done

Before you go in front of your friends, rub some soap on the bottom of the plate. Use a bar of soap to do this. Then press a penny against the soap on the plate to make it stick. Nobody knows about *this* penny. What about the other one? You only pretend to wrap it in the paper, but you really let that penny slip out and fall into your lap.

When you tap the plate, push the plate a little. The penny that is stuck on it will rub against the rim of the glass. It will come loose and fall into the glass.

This is your last trick. When it is over, take a bow and walk off the stage.

Comprehension Check

1. What makes the ruler rise from your hand?
2. Why does the penny stick to the bottom of the plate?
3. Which of the tricks do you think was the best? Why do you feel as you do?
4. What kind of magic trick would you like to do?

Skill Check

1. Look back to page 245. What is the first thing to do in this trick? What is the second thing to do? What should you do last?
2. What is the last thing to do in your magic show?

The One in the Middle Is a Green Kangaroo

by Judy Blume

Freddy Dissel had two problems. One was his older brother Mike. The other was his younger sister Ellen. Freddy thought a lot about being the one in the middle. But there was nothing he could do about it. He felt like the peanut-butter part of a sandwich, squeezed between Mike and Ellen.

Every year Mike got new clothes. He grew too big for his old ones. But Mike's old clothes weren't too small for Freddy. They fit him just fine.

Freddy used to have a room of his own. That was before Ellen was born. Now Ellen had a room of *her* own. Freddy moved in with Mike. Mr. and Mrs. Dissel said, "It's the boys' room." But they couldn't fool Freddy. He knew better!

Then Freddy Dissel heard about the school play. Mike had never been in a play. Ellen had never been in a play. This was his chance to do something special. Freddy decided he would try it.

He waited two whole days before he went to his teacher. "Miss Gumber," he said, "I want to be in the school play."

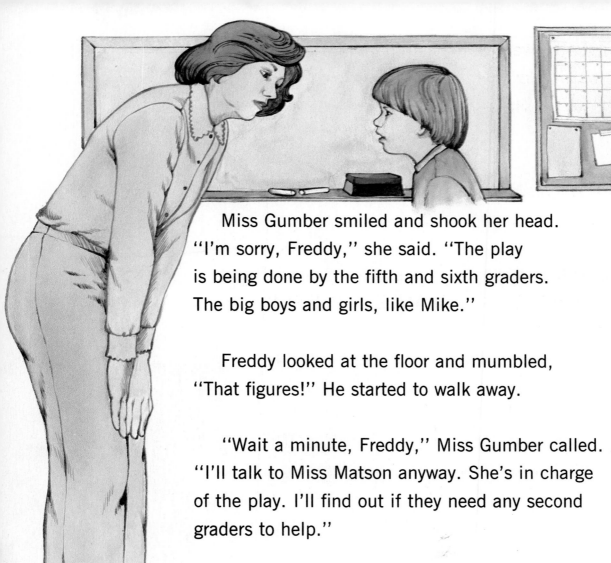

Miss Gumber smiled and shook her head.
"I'm sorry, Freddy," she said. "The play
is being done by the fifth and sixth graders.
The big boys and girls, like Mike."

Freddy looked at the floor and mumbled,
"That figures!" He started to walk away.

"Wait a minute, Freddy," Miss Gumber called.
"I'll talk to Miss Matson anyway. She's in charge
of the play. I'll find out if they need any second
graders to help."

Miss Gumber went away for a few minutes.
When she came back she said, "Miss Matson
needs someone to play a special part. Go to the
auditorium this afternoon. Maybe you'll get the
part."

"Oh, boy!" Freddy hollered.

250

Later he went to the auditorium. Miss Matson was waiting for him. Freddy walked right up close to her. He said, "I want to be in the play."

Miss Matson asked him to go up on the stage and say that again in a very loud voice.

Freddy climbed onto the stage and shouted, "I AM FREDDY. I WANT TO BE IN THE PLAY."

"Good," Miss Matson called. "Now then, Freddy, can you jump?"

What kind of question was that, Freddy wondered. Of course he could jump. He was in the second grade, wasn't he? So he jumped. He jumped all around the stage—big jumps and little jumps.

When he was through, Miss Matson said, "I think you will be fine as the Green Kangaroo, Freddy. It's a very important part."

Freddy didn't tell anyone at home about the play until dinnertime. Then Freddy said, "Guess what, everyone? I'm going to be in a play. I'm going to be the Green Kangaroo!"

"What did you say?" Mike asked.

"I said I'm going to be in the school play. I said I'm going to be the Green Kangaroo!"

"It can't be true," Mike yelled. "You? Why would they pick you?"

Freddy told them just how he got the part.
"It's really true," he said. "Just me. All by
myself. The only Green Kangaroo in the play."

"That sounds wonderful," his dad said with
a big smile.

And his mom kissed him right at the dinner
table. "We're all proud of you, Freddy," she
said.

Ellen was excited too. She kept laughing.
But Mike just shook his head and repeated,
"Wow! He's going to be the Green Kangaroo!"

254

The next two weeks were busy ones for Freddy. He had to practice being the Green Kangaroo a lot. He practiced at school on the stage. He practiced at home too. He made kangaroo faces in front of the mirror. He did kangaroo jumps on his bed. He even dreamed about Green Kangaroos at night.

Finally the day of the play came. After lunch Miss Gumber called to Freddy, "Time to go now. Time to get into your costume." Miss Gumber walked to the hall with Freddy. Then she whispered, "We'll be in the second row. Good luck."

Freddy went to Miss Matson's room. Some of the sixth graders had made his costume. They all giggled when Miss Matson helped Freddy into it. His Green Kangaroo suit covered all of him. It even had green feet. Only his face stuck out. Miss Matson put some green dots on it.

Miss Matson laughed. "We'll wash the dots off later. OK?"

"OK," Freddy mumbled. He jumped over to the mirror and looked at himself. He really felt like a Green Kangaroo.

256

It was time for the play to begin. Freddy
waited backstage with the fifth and sixth
graders who were in the play.

And then it was his turn. He jumped out onto
the stage and looked out into the audience. All
those people were down there—somewhere. He knew
they were. It was very quiet. He could hear his
heart. He thought he saw his mom and dad. He
thought he saw Ellen. He thought he saw Mike and
his second-grade class and Miss Gumber and all
of the neighbors too. They were all out there
somewhere. They were all in the middle of the
audience. But Freddy wasn't in the middle. He
was all by himself up on the stage. He had a job
to do. He *had* to be the Green Kangaroo.

Freddy smiled. His heart slowed down. His stomach stayed still. He felt better. He smiled a bigger, wider smile. He felt good.

"HELLO, EVERYONE," Freddy said. "I AM THE GREEN KANGAROO. WELCOME."

The play began. Freddy did his little jumps. Every now and then one of the fifth or sixth graders in the play said to him, "And who are you?"

Freddy jumped around and answered, "Me? I am the Green Kangaroo!" Every time he said it the audience laughed. Freddy liked it when they laughed.

When it was all over, everyone on the stage took a bow. Then Miss Matson came out and said, "A special thank you to our second grader, Freddy Dissel. He played the part of the Green Kangaroo."

Freddy jumped over to the middle of the stage. He took a big, low bow all by himself. The audience clapped hard for a long time.

Freddy didn't care much about wearing Mike's clothes anymore. He didn't care much about sharing Mike's room either. He didn't even care much about being the one in the middle. He felt just great being Freddy Dissel.

audience

barley   2.

A a

---

an tique something, such as a table, a bowl, or any piece of furniture, that was made long ago. **an tiques.**

au di ence a group of people who come together to watch or listen to something: *The audience liked the play.* See the picture. **au di enc es**

B b

---

bar ley 1. the grain of a plant, used for food. **2.** the plant. See the picture.

C c

---

clev er 1. bright; having a good mind. **2.** able to do something very well: *Kit is a clever artist.* **clev er er, clev er est.**

clo ver a plant with sweet-smelling red or white flowers. See the picture. **clo vers.**

cross 1. move from one side to another: *I crossed the street.* **2.** one stick with another across it to form a + or an ✕. **3.** mark with an ✕ or draw a line through: *Mario crossed out his mistake.* **4.** feeling angry: *The baby was cross because he was hungry.* **crossed, cross ing; cross es; cross er, cross est.**

D d

dan de li on a plant with a bright yellow flower. See the picture. **dan de li ons.**

dove a bird with a thick body. See the picture. **doves.** (*Dove* rhymes with *love.*)

E e

either 1. one or the other of two: *A window is either shut or open.* **2.** each of two: *There are trees on either side of the street.*

e nor mous very, very large.

ex cept other than: *This store is open every day except Sunday.*

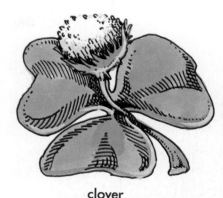

clover

dandelion

dove

forest

F f

fact a thing that can be proved to be true: *It's a fact that Tuesday always comes after Monday.* **facts.**

fa mous very well known; important: *The President of the United States is a famous person.*

fi nal ly at the end; at last: *Our team finally won a game.*

for est thick woods, often covering many miles. See the picture. **for ests.**

fu ture the time to come; what is to come: *I will take a trip to Spain someday in the future.*

G g

guess 1. think without really knowing: *I guess it will rain tomorrow.* 2. an idea you have that may not be right: *My guess is that the tree is ten feet high.* **guessed, guess ing; guess es.**

ground 1. the earth that we walk on: *The ground was hard and rocky.* 2. on the ground: *the ground floor of a building.* 3. crushed into small pieces: *He went to buy ground meat.*

guide **1.** show the way or lead someone: *The dog will guide us back to our house.* **2.** someone or something that leads you or shows the way: *The guide showed us around the park.* **guid ed, guid ing; guides.**

H h

---

health being well or being sick: *When you are sick, you are not in good health.*

I i

---

im pos si ble something that cannot be or happen: *It is impossible for a cow to jump over the moon.*

in ven tion something that a person thinks of or makes that is new: *People had to read by candlelight before the invention of the light bulb.* **in ven tions.**

J j

---

jar **1.** something that holds things and is often made of glass. See the picture. **2.** shake or rattle: *Don't jar the desk while I write.* **jars; jarred, jar ring.**

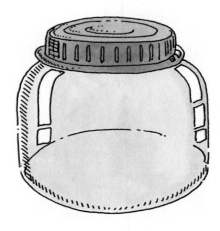

jar 1.

knee

lizard

magnify

K k

knee the middle part of the leg. See the picture. **knees.**

L l

liz ard an animal like a snake, but with four legs and a long tail. See the picture. **liz ards.**

M m

mag ni fi cent beautiful to see: *The queen lived in a magnificent palace.*

mag ni fy make something look or seem larger than it really is: *Magnify the ants and they will look very large.* See the picture. **mag ni fied, mag ni fy ing.**

mys ter i ous hard to understand or explain: *She heard a mysterious noise.*

N n

nar ra tor a person who tells a story. **nar ra tors.**

O o

ocean a great body of salt water. Oceans cover a large part of the earth. **oceans.**

oc to pus a sea animal. It has a soft, thick body and eight arms. See the picture. **oc to pus es.**

Ohio one of the fifty states of the United States.

opos sum a small animal that can hang by its tail and carries its young on its back. When it is caught, it pretends to be dead. See the picture. **opos sums.**

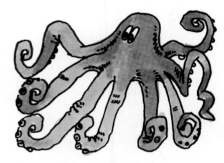

octopus

opossum

P p

pink **1.** light red; the color made by mixing red with white. **2.** having this color. **pinks; pink er, pink est.**

place **1.** a building: *My home is the place where I live.* **2.** the spot that a person or thing is on: *The book is in its place.* **3.** in a game or contest, the spot each person finishes in: *Sue won the race, so she was in first place.* **plac es; placed, plac ing.**

po et ry the result of arranging words in verse.

puz zle **1.** a problem or task to be done for fun: *Suki was working on a puzzle.* **2.** a hard problem. **3.** be unable to understand something: *How the mouse got in puzzled us.* **puz zles; puz zled, puz zling.**

Q q

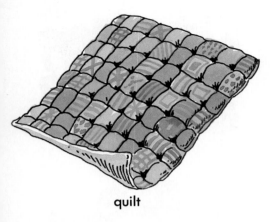

quilt

quilt a thick cover for a bed, usually made from colorful pieces of cloth sewn together. See the picture. **quilts.**

R r

raccoon

rac coon a small animal that sleeps in the daytime and comes out at night. See the picture. **rac coons.**

re pair **1.** put something in good shape again: *Will you repair my torn coat?* **2.** the work of putting something in good shape again: *We finished the repairs on her car.* **re paired, re pair ing; re pairs.**

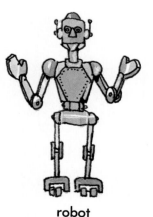

robot

ro bot a machine made of metal that looks like a person. It does not think but does whatever people tell it to do. See the picture. **ro bots.**

rul er 1. a straight piece of wood or metal that we use to see how long something is. See the picture. 2. a king, queen, or anyone who is the head of a country. **rul ers.**

ruler 1.

S s

sim ple 1. easy to do or understand: *Steve learned to play a simple song on the piano.* 2. plain; without anything extra. **sim pler, sim plest.**

spark 1. a bright flash: *Sparks of color lit up the night.* 2. a small bit of fire: *The sparks jumped off the burning wood.* **sparks.**

spring 1. the season of the year when plants begin to grow. 2. jump; rise or move suddenly: *Watch me spring into the air.* 3. a small stream of water coming out of the ground. **sprang, sprung, spring ing; springs.**

sta tion 1. a place where television or radio shows are sent out. 2. a place used for something special: *a gas station, a railroad station.* **sta tions.**

stoop 1. steps leading up to a house: *My friends were sitting on the stoop.* 2. bend the body over: *I stooped to pick up the papers.* **stoops; stooped, stoop ing.**

stu dio **1.** a room where television or radio shows are put on the air. **2.** a room where an artist works. **3.** a place where movies are made. **stu di os.**

T   t

---

thought what someone thinks; thinking about something: *Pam had a sudden thought. Give this problem a lot of thought.* **thoughts.**

thrush a bird that sings. See the picture. **thrush es.**

thrush

U   u

---

un cle your father's or mother's brother or your aunt's husband. **un cles.**

V   v

---

vi bra tion a shaking; a moving back and forth very, very fast: *We could feel the vibration of the floor as the truck went by.* **vi bra tions.**

W w

wood chuck a small animal with a bushy tail. See the picture. **wood chucks.**

wood peck er a bird with a hard, pointed bill for making holes in trees to get insects. **wood peck ers**

woodchuck

X x

X ray a picture that shows what is inside something. See the picture. **X rays.**

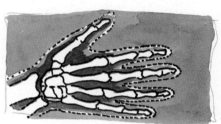

X ray

Y y

yard **1.** the ground around a building: *You can play in the front yard.* **2.** a measurement of 3 feet or 36 inches. **yards.**

Z z

ze bra a wild animal, something like a horse, but with black and white stripes. See the picture. **ze bras.**

zebra

MASTERY WORD LIST

The following words have been read enough times for pupils to reach mastery by the end of this book. Pupils will be able to recognize both the root word and the root word with these endings and spelling changes: *s*, *es*, *ed*, *ing*, *'s*, *er*, *est*, *en*; final consonant doubled, final *e* dropped.

The number after each word shows the page on which the word first appears as a mastery word in this book. For a cumulative list of mastery words see the Teacher's Edition for *Rainbow Shower*.

frog 8	everybody 28	rule 46	advice 67
garden 8	grandma 28	sorry 46	bad 67
hard 8	him 28	ten 46	cousin 67
toad 8	mean 28	happen 47	forest 67
cried 9	sister 28	choose 48	meet 67
ground 9	teeth 28	easy 48	middle 67
seed 9	uncle 28	hundred 48	problem 67
afraid 10	hall 30	mountain 48	sitting 67
shout 10	knew 30	pocket 49	daddy 69
story 11	nobody 30	perfect 50	monkey 71
decide 18	paper 30	color 51	blind 79
maybe 18	piece 30	cape 56	city 79
mind 18	taped 30	smiled 56	early 79
morning 18	written 30	waved 56	feel 79
pleased 18	brother 38	cheer 57	spring 79
wonder 18	every 38	except 57	country 80
somebody 20	poem 38	scarves 57	guide 80
store 20	secret 38	trick 57	month 80
newspaper 21	wrote 38	ever 58	young 80
parrot 21	family 39	quiet 58	hug 81
flew 23	proud 39	rabbit 58	love 81
popcorn 23	writing 39	seen 58	car 83
whatever 23	children 40	silly 58	cross 83
splash 24	poetry 41	learn 59	safe 83
floated 25	friend 46	reach 59	street 83
else 28	rock 46	ready 59	beach 87

A separate group of skill-related words appears below. Pupils will be able to recognize these terms.

(Acknowledgments continued from page 2)

"The Magic Spectacles" is based on a story from THE MAGIC SPECTACLES and other easy-to-read stories by Lilian Moore. Copyright © 1965 by Lilian Moore. By permission of Four Winds Press, a Division of Scholastic Magazines, Inc.

"Fast and Slow" from FAST AND SLOW by John Ciardi. Copyright © 1975 by John Ciardi. Reprinted by permission of Houghton Mifflin Company.

"Plants Do Strange Things," adapted by permission of Alfred A. Knopf, Inc., from PLANTS DO AMAZING THINGS, by Hedda Nussbaum. Copyright © 1977 by Random House, Inc.

"Two Good Friends" is taken from TWO GOOD FRIENDS by Judy Delton. Text copyright © 1974 by Judy Delton. Used by permission of Crown Publishers, Inc.

"Surprise from a hat" and "Drop a penny through a plate" from FUNNY MAGIC—Easy Tricks for Young Magicians by Rose Wyler and Gerald Ames. Text copyright © 1972 by Rose Wyler & Gerald Ames. By permission of Four Winds Press, a division of Scholastic Magazines, Inc., and the authors.

"The One in the Middle Is a Green Kangaroo" adapted from THE ONE IN THE MIDDLE IS A GREEN KANGAROO by Judy Blume. Copyright © 1969 by Judy Blume. Reprinted by permission of Harold Ober Associates Incorporated.

Glossary entries taken or adapted from MY SECOND PICTURE DICTIONARY. Copyright © 1975, 1971 Scott, Foresman and Company. All Rights Reserved.

ILLUSTRATIONS

Cover: Kinuko Craft
Karen Ackoff: pages 155–161; Angela Adams: 46–54; Michael Adams: 79–86; Bob Barner: 16–17, 35–37, 65–66, 100–101, 117–118, 162–163, 193–194, 208–210, 232–234; Marc Brown: 109–116; Pam Carroll: 211–217; Len Ebert: 173–182; Len Epstein: 129–140; Jon R. Freidman: 225; George Gershinowitz: 226–231; Ronald Himler: 38–45; Troy Howell: 55; Dora Leder: 28–34;

Ron LeHew: 18–27; Susan Lexa: 87–97, 142–153; Arnold Lobel: 8–14; Giulio Maestro: 235–241; Les Morrill: 154, 192; Carol Newsom: 249–259, Carol Nicklaus: 56–64, 67–78; Stella Ormai: 218–224; Nancy Schill: 202–207; Jacqueline Smith: 119–128; Roslyn Streifer: 243; Joe Veno: 195–201, 260–269; David Weisner: 15; Jennie Williams: 164–172; Lane Yerkes: 183–191.

PHOTOGRAPHS

Douglas Keister: pages 98–99; Barbara Kirk: 242–248; Stephan Tur: 102–108.

STUDIO

Kirchoff/Wohlberg, Inc.